Home Design: 55 Skippy 2 Bed

FEATURES

- 2 Bedroom
- 2 Wardrobes
- Kitchen
- Bathroom / Laundry

Feet & Inches
Living Area: 473 Sq. Ft
Total Area: 590 Sq. Ft

Metric Sizes
Living Area: 49.8 m2
Total Area: 55.06 m2

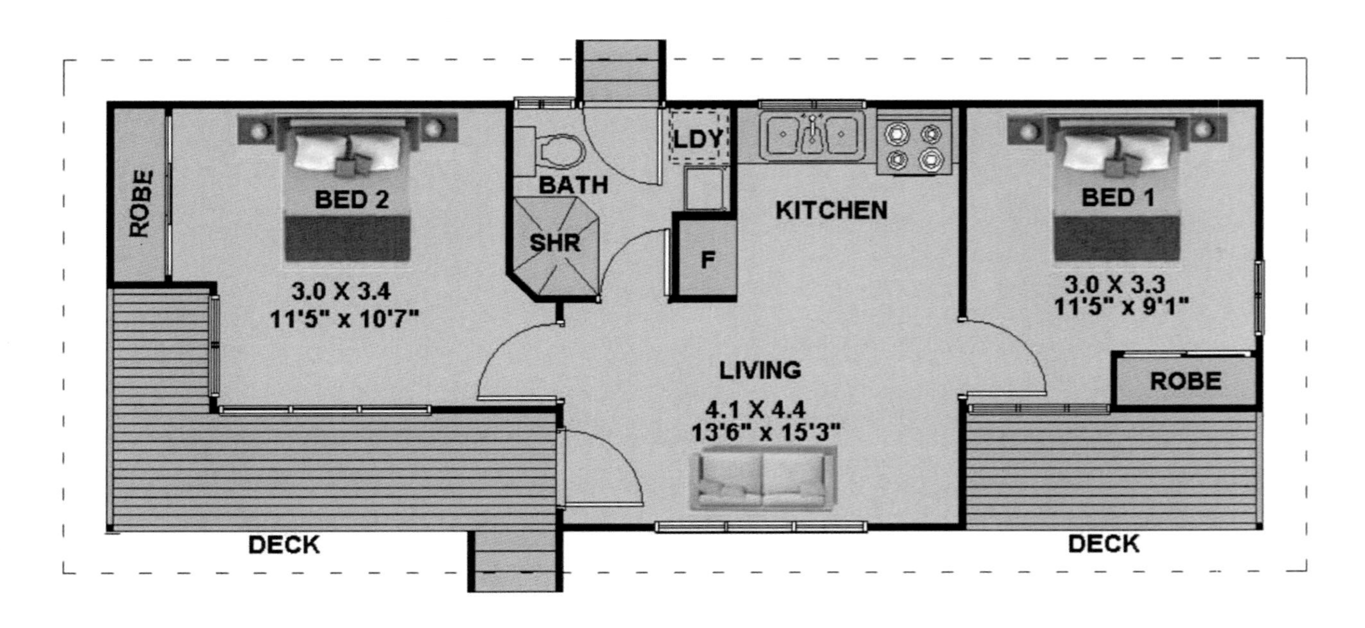

Do you want this plan? See our Website to Upgrade to Our Low Cost Concept Plans

Feet Width 15'3" x 39'4" **Width 12.0 x 4.64 Meters**

www.australianfloorplans.com.au

Home Design: 59 Tamika   2 Bed + 2 Bath + Large Living + Carport

Feet & Inches
Floor Area: 641 Sq Ft
Carport : 236 Sq Ft
Total Area: 1140 Sq Ft

FEATURES
- 2 Bedroom
- 2 Bathrooms
- Carport
- Kitchen
- Large Living Area

Metric Sizes
Floor Area: **59.61 m2**
Carport : 22.22 m2
Total Area: 106.23 m2

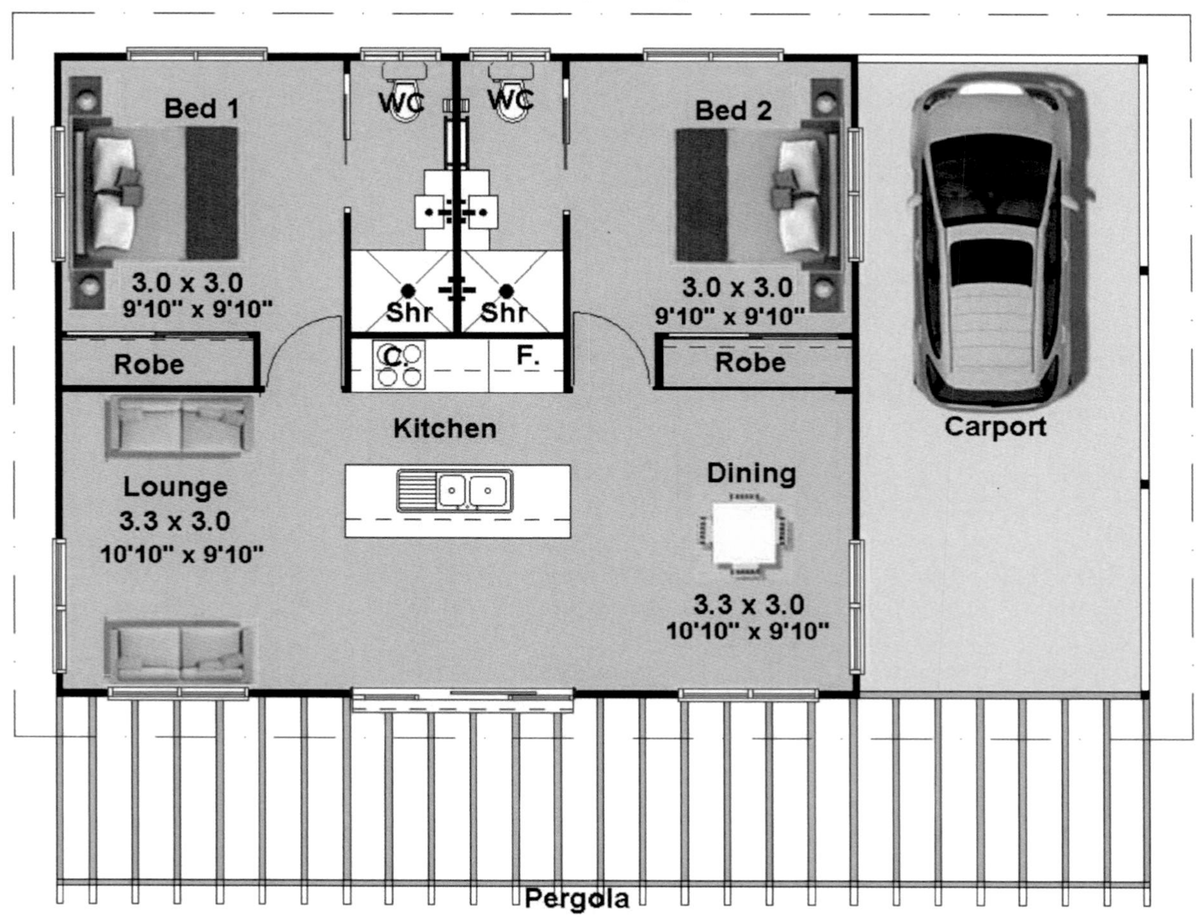

Do you want this plan? See our Website to Upgrade to Our Low Cost Concept Plans

Feet Width 30'3" x 38'2"   **Width 11.64 x 9.2 Meters**

www.australianfloorplans.com.au

Rosebud Design RH: 59.4 2 Bed + Large Bath + Large Living

Feet & Inches

Floor : 620.9 Sq Ft

Verandah : 340.9 Sq Ft

Total Area: 961.8 Sq Ft

FEATURES

- 2 Bedroom
- Large Bathroom
- Kitchen -Meals
- Large Living
- Raked Ceiling

Metric Sizes

Floor : 59.4 m2

Verandah : 31.4 m2

Total Area: 90.8 m2

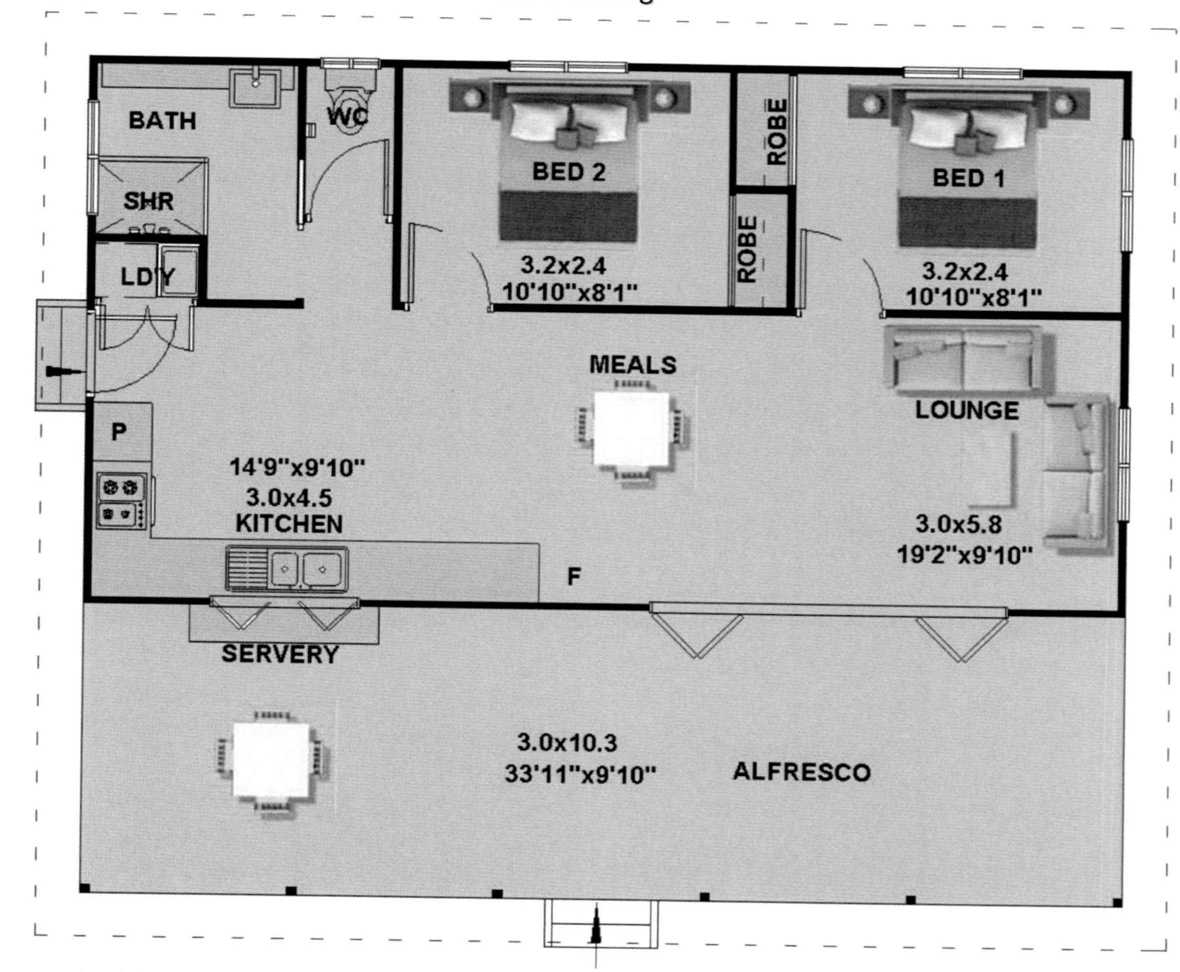

Do you want this plan? See our Website to Upgrade to Our Low Cost Concept Plans

Feet Width 34'4" x 28''5" **Width 10.47 x 8.67 Meters**

www.australianfloorplans.com.au

Rosebud Design LH: 59.4 2 Bed + Large Bath + Large Living

Feet & Inches
Floor : 620.9 Sq Ft
Verandah : 340.9 Sq Ft
Total Area: 961.8 Sq Ft

FEATURES
- 2 Bedroom
- Large Bathroom
- Kitchen -Meals
- Large Living
- Raked Ceiling

Metric Sizes
Floor : 59.4 m2
Verandah : 31.4 m2
Total Area: 90.8 m2

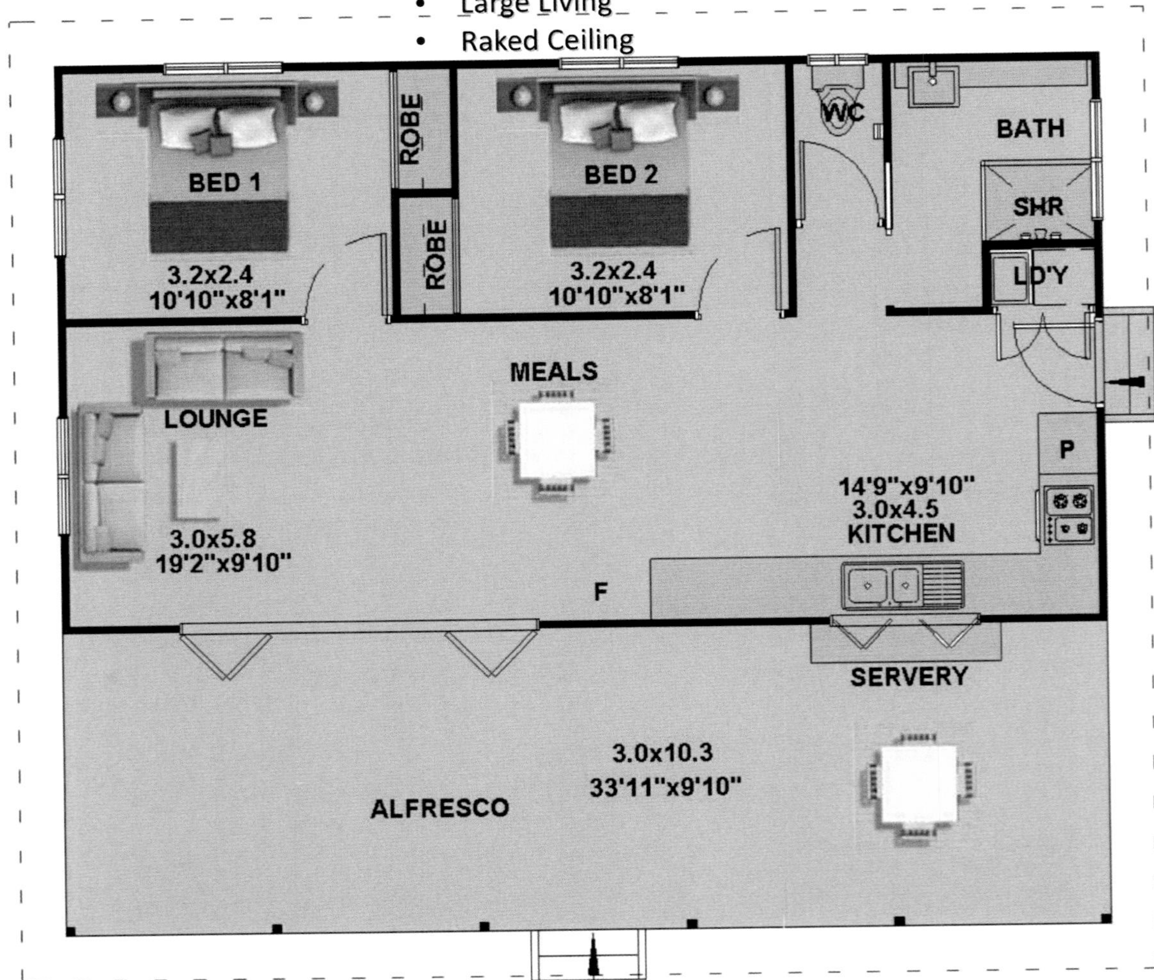

Feet Width 34'4" x 28"5" **Width 10.47 x 8.67 Meters**

Home Design: 59.8 Beach **2 Bed + Bath + 2 Decks + Raked Ceiling**

FEATURES

- 2 Bedroom
- Bathroom + Sep Laundry
- Great Room
- 2 Decks
- High Raked Ceiling

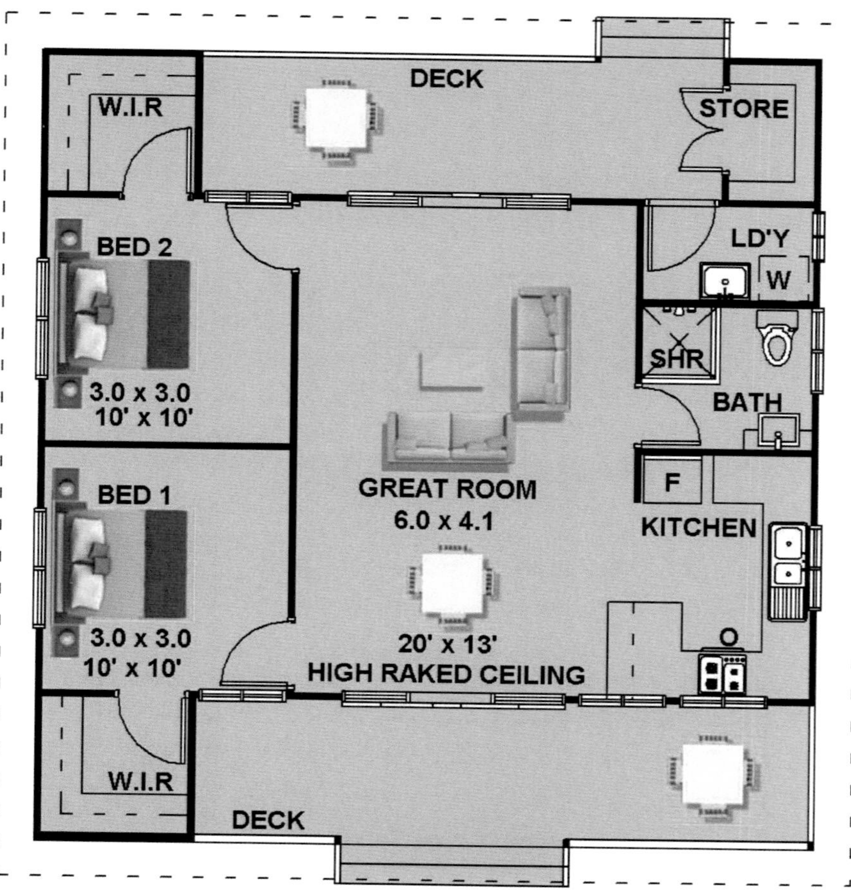

Feet & Inches

Floor Area: 718 Sq Feet
Deck Area: 294 Sq Feet
Total Area: 1012 Sq Feet

Metric Sizes

Floor Area: 66.7 m2
Deck Area: 27.35m2
Total Area: 94.05 m2

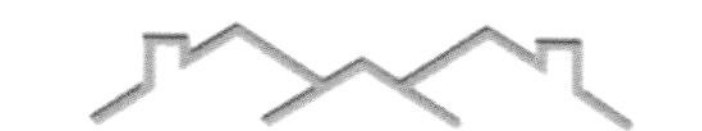

Australian Design Services
A Design World Of Difference

Do you want this plan? See our Website to Upgrade to Our Low Cost Concept Plans

Feet Width 31' 2" x 32' 4 " **Width 9.5 x 9.9 Meters**

www.australianfloorplans.com.au

Narrow Lot Design RH: 59.9 Bay Cottage 2 Bed+ Large Living

Feet & Inches
Living Area: 644.0 Sq. Ft
Deck Area : 376.0 Sq. Ft
Porch Area : 67.0 Sq. Ft
Total Area: 1089 Sq. Ft

FEATURES
- 2 Bedroom
- Large Bathroom-Laundry
- Kitchen -Meals
- Large Living
- Deck on 3 Sides

Metric Sizes
Living Area: 59.9 m2
Deck Area : 35.0 m2
Porch Area : 6.3 m2
Total Area: 101.2 m2

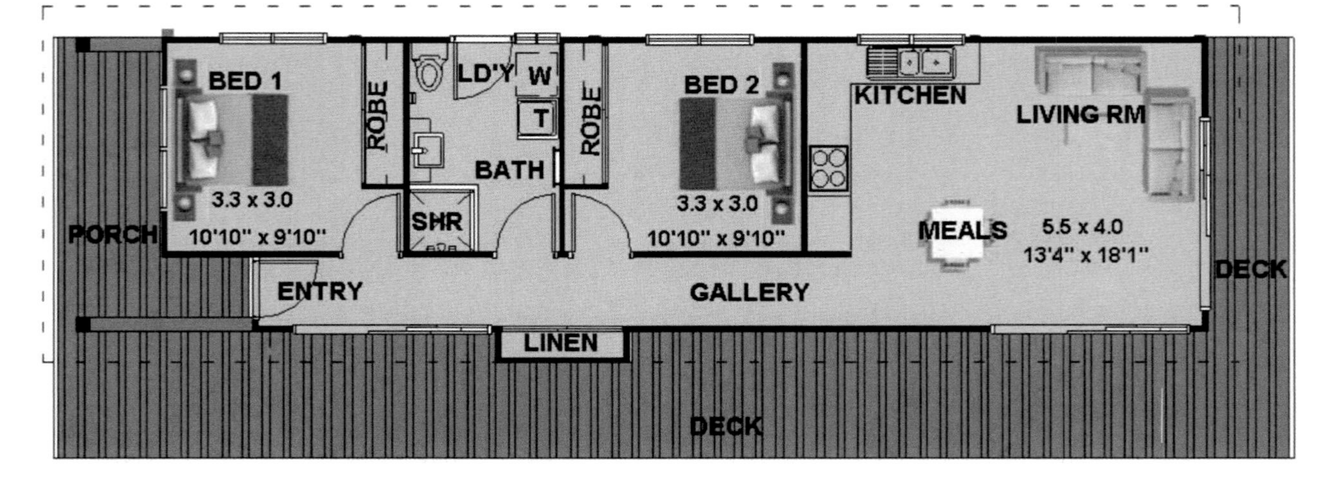

Do you want this plan? See our Website to Upgrade to Our Low Cost Concept Plans

Feet Width 19'9" x 56' 7" **Width 6.0 x 17.2 Meters**

www.australianfloorplans.com.au

Narrow Lot Design LH: 59.9 Bay Cottage 2 Bed+ Large Living

Feet & Inches

Living Area: 644.0 Sq. Ft
Deck Area : 376.0 Sq. Ft
Porch Area : 67.0 Sq. Ft
Total Area: 1089 Sq. Ft

FEATURES

- 2 Bedroom
- Large Bathroom-Laundry
- Kitchen -Meals
- Large Living
- Deck on 3 Sides

Metric Sizes

Living Area: 59.9 m2
Deck Area : 35.0 m2
Porch Area : 6.3 m2
Total Area: 101.2 m2

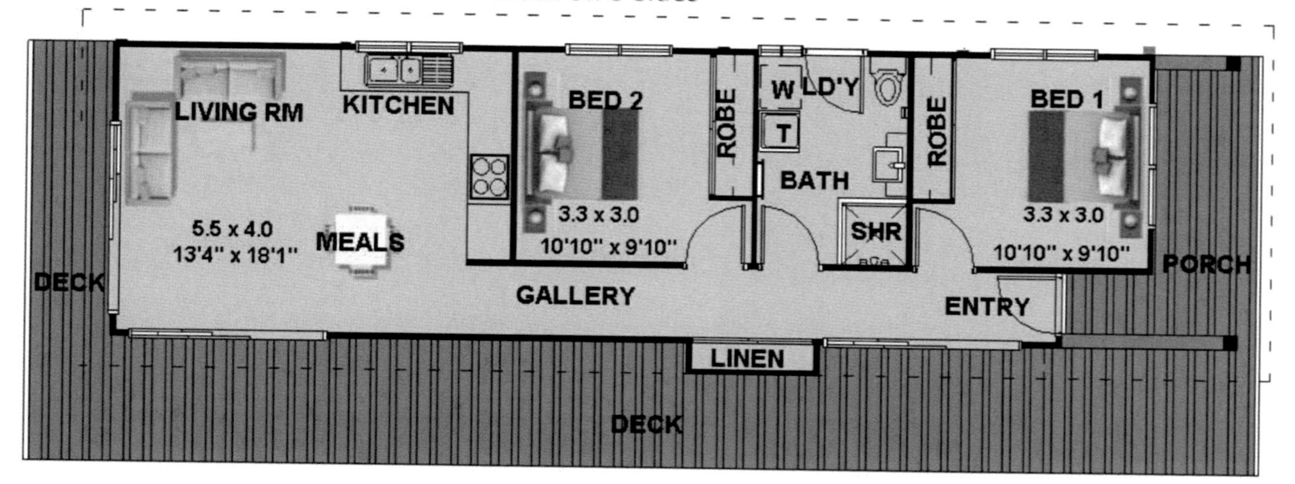

Do you want this plan? See our Website to Upgrade to Our Low Cost Concept Plans

Feet Width 19'9" x 56' 7" **Width 6.0 x 17.2 Meters**

www.australianfloorplans.com.au

Home Design: 59.8 Sea-crest 2 Bed + Study Nook + Deck

FEATURES

- 2 Bedroom
- Bathroom
- Study Nook
- Large Deck

Feet & Inches

Living area : 627 Sq. Ft
Deck : 466 Sq. Ft
Total Area: 1093 Sq. Ft

Metric Sizes

Living Area: 59.8 m2
Deck Area: 25.7 m2
Total Area: 85.54 m2

Australian Design Services
A Design World Of Difference

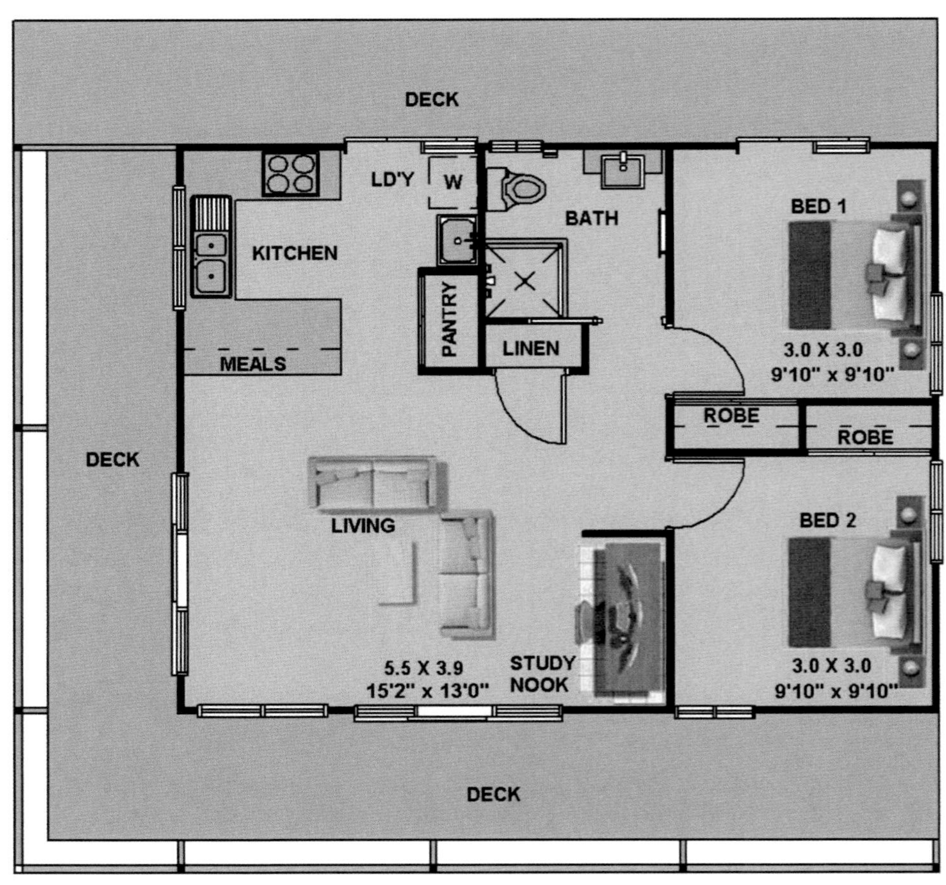

Do you want this plan? See our Website to Upgrade to Our Low Cost Concept Plans

Feet Width 35'1" x 33'6" Width 10.69 x 10.2 Meters

www.australianfloorplans.com.au

Home Design: IMR 59.9 RH

2 Bed + 1 Bath + 2 Living Areas

Feet & Inches

Living area : 645 Sq. Ft
Porch : 16 Sq. Ft
Total Area: 660 Sq. Ft

FEATURES

- 2 Bedroom
- 1 Bathroom
- Kitchen
- Separate Laundry
- 2 Living Areas

Metric Sizes

Living Area: 59.9 m2
Porch : 1.5 m2
Total Area: 61.4 m2

Australian Design Services
A Design World Of Difference

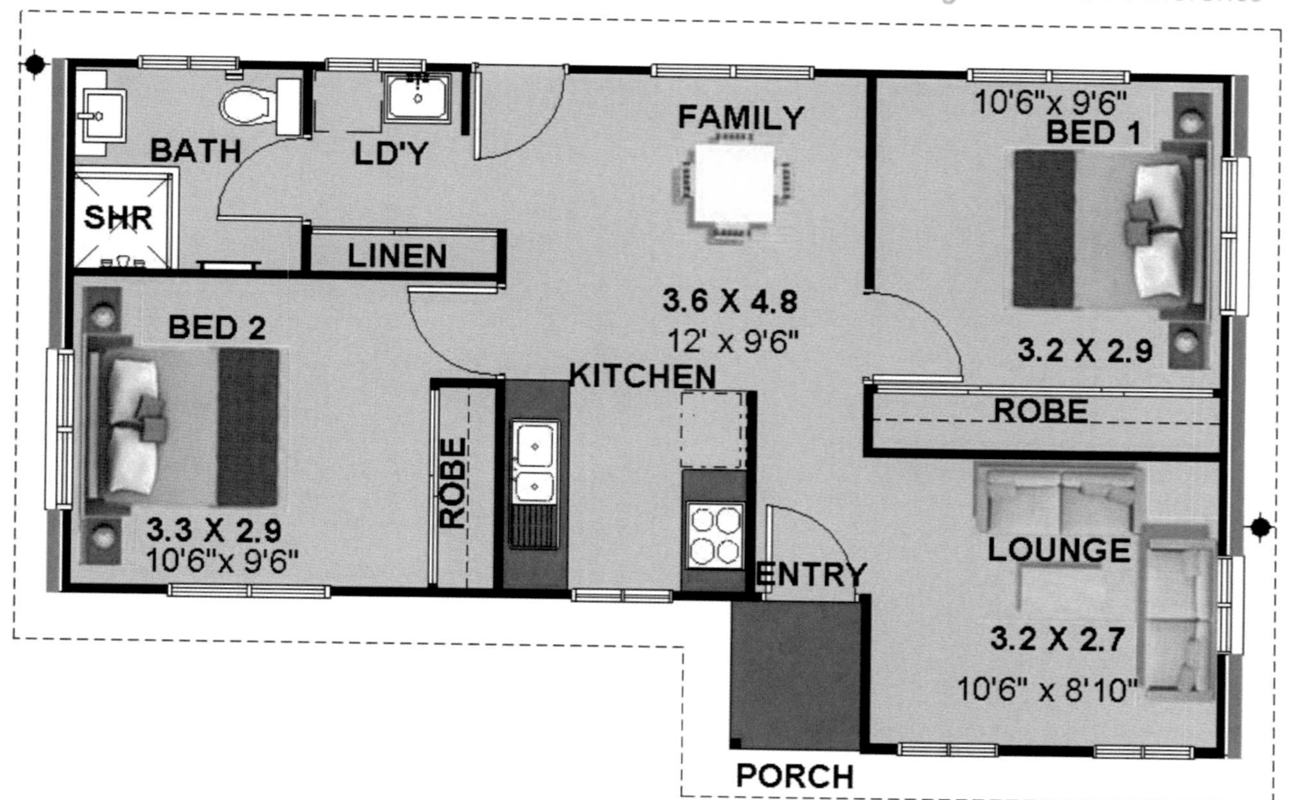

Do you want this plan? See our Website to Upgrade to Our Low Cost Concept Plans

Feet Width 36' x 21 ' **Width 11.0 x 6.4 Meters**

www.australianfloorplans.com.au

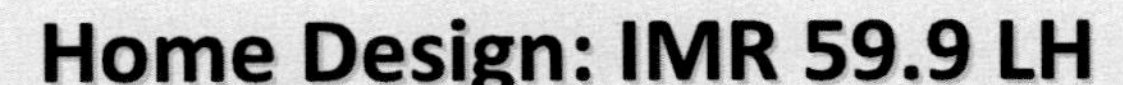

2 Bed + 1 Bath + 2 Living Areas

Feet & Inches

Living area : 645 Sq. Ft
Porch : 16 Sq. Ft
Total Area: 660 Sq. Ft

FEATURES

- 2 Bedroom
- 1 Bathroom
- Kitchen
- Separate Laundry
- 2 Living Areas

Metric Sizes

Living Area: 59.9 m2
Porch : 1.5 m2
Total Area: 61.4 m2

Australian Design Services
A Design World Of Difference

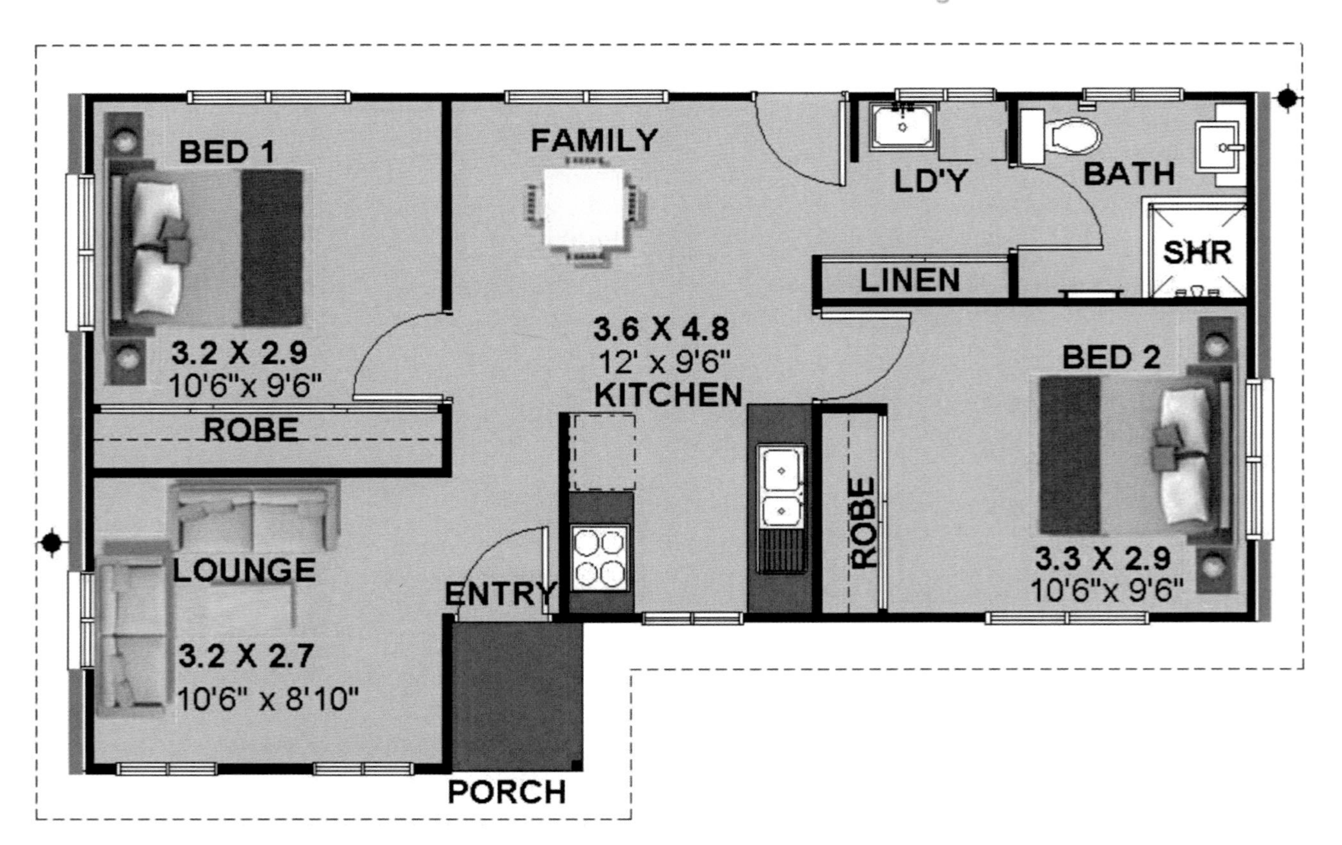

Feet Width 36' x 21 ' **Width 11.0 x 6.4 Meters**

Home Design: 60 Freedom

2 Bed + 1 Bath + Transportable

Feet & Inches

Living area : 529 Sq. Ft
Deck Area: 20 Sq. Ft
Total Area: 644 Sq. Ft

FEATURES

- Transportable Design
- 2 Bedroom
- Bath / Laundry
- Kitchen
- Fold up Deck

Metric Sizes

Living Area: 58.10 m2
Deck Area: 1.9 m2
Total Area: 59.9 m2

Australian Design Services
A Design World Of Difference

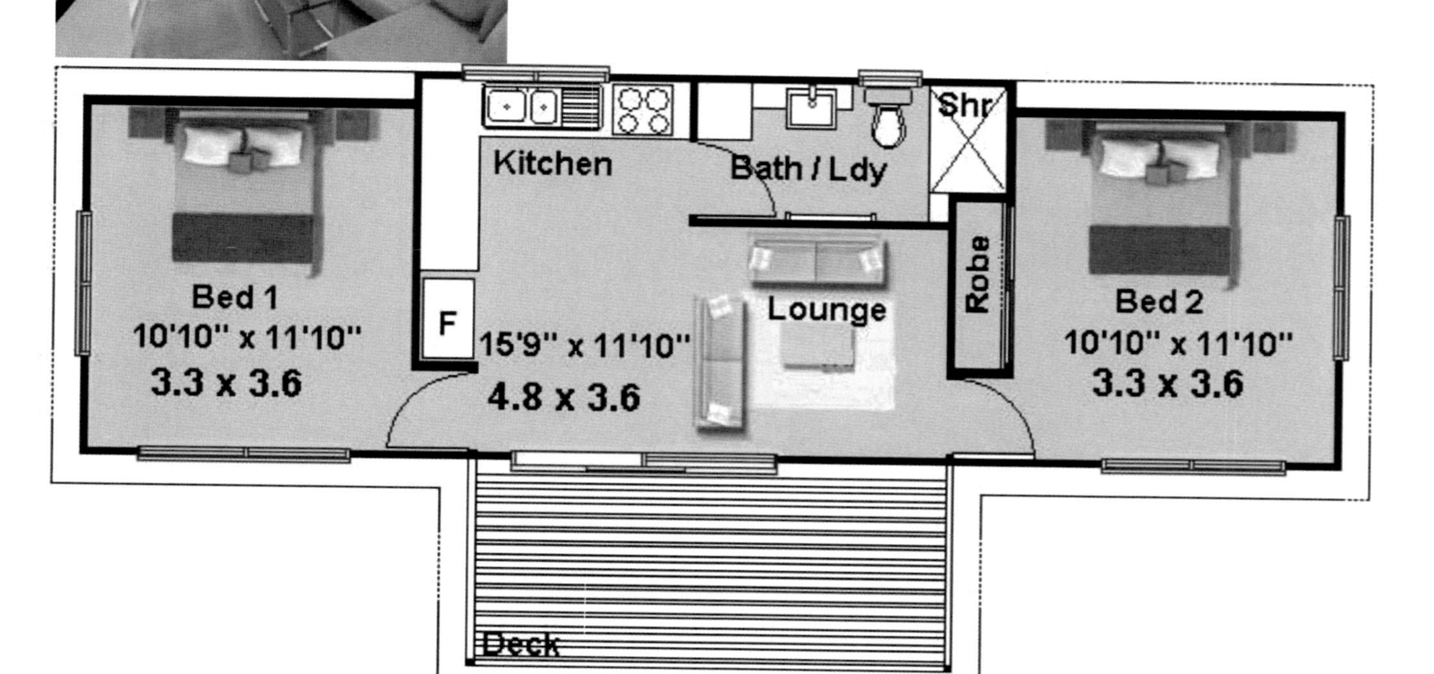

Do you want this plan? See our Website to Upgrade to Our Low Cost Concept Plans

Feet Width 42'3" x 21'4" **Width 6.5 x 12.8 Meters**

www.australianfloorplans.com.au

Home Design: 60 SBH-RH

2 Bed + Study Nook + Alfresco

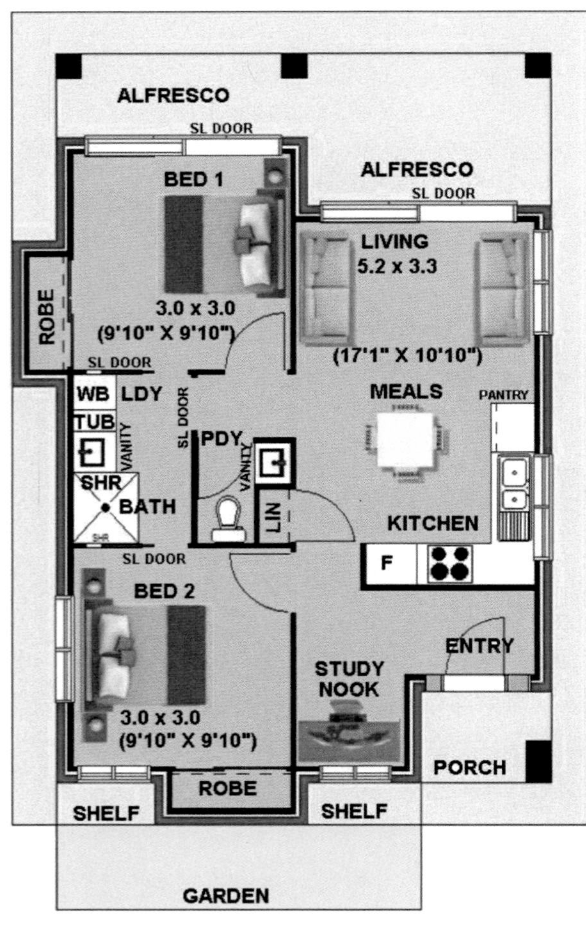

Australian Design Services

A Design World Of Difference

FEATURES

- 2 Bedroom + Study Nook
- Large Bathroom + Laundry Area
- Open Kitchen + Meals Area
- Large Living
- Large Alfresco
- Impressive facade and Porch

Feet & Inches	**Metric Sizes**
Living: 648 Sq. Ft	Living: 59.8 m2
Alfresco : .125 Sq. Ft	Alfresco : 12.06 m2
Porch : 25 Sq. Ft	Porch : 2.34 m2
Total Area: 798 Sq. Ft	**Total Area: 74.20 m2**

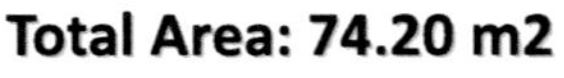

Do you want this plan? See our Website to Upgrade to Our Low Cost Concept Plans

Feet Width 24'5" x 35' 9" **Width 6.83 x 11.0 Meters**

www.australianfloorplans.com.au

Home Design: 60 SBH-LH **2 Bed + Study Nook + Alfresco**

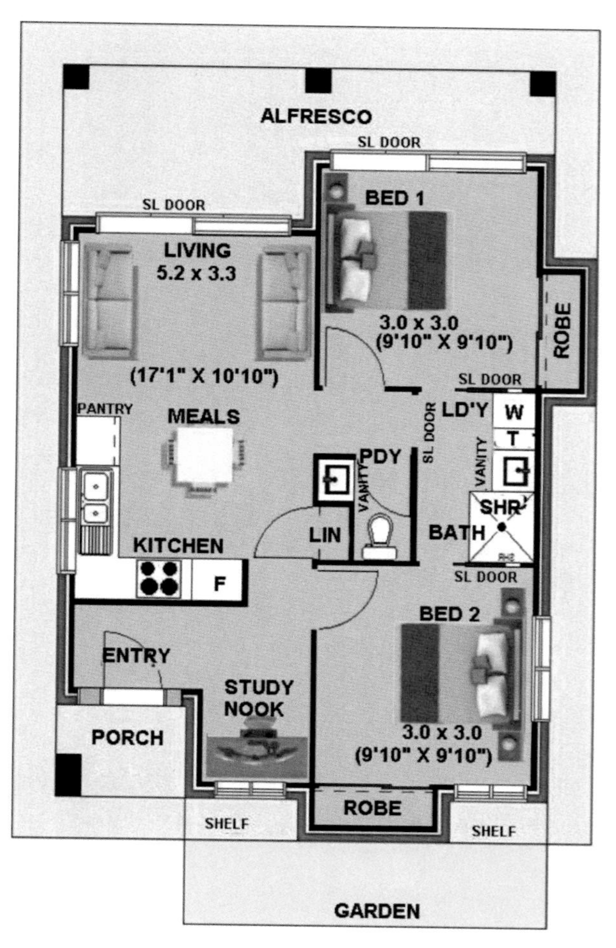

Australian Design Services

A Design World Of Difference

FEATURES

- 2 Bedroom + Study Nook
- Large Bathroom + Laundry Area
- Open Kitchen + Meals Area
- Large Living
- Large Alfresco
- Impressive facade and Porch

Feet & Inches	**Metric Sizes**
Living: 648 Sq. Ft	Living: 59.8 m2
Alfresco : .125 Sq. Ft	Alfresco : 12.06 m2
Porch : 25 Sq. Ft	Porch : 2.34 m2
Total Area: 798 Sq. Ft	**Total Area: 74.20 m2**

Like this plan? Upgrade to: architectural preliminary plans **More Information** CLICK HERE

Feet Width 24'5" x 35' 9" **Width 6.83 x 11.0 Meters**

www.australianfloorplans.com.au

Home Design: New Age 63.9 RH 2 Bed + 1 Bath + Large Living

FEATURES

- 2 Bedroom
- Large Bathroom
- Kitchen Laundry Combo
- Porch Area

Feet & Inches

Living area : 636 Sq. Ft
Deck Area : 52 Sq. Ft
Total Area: 688 Sq. Ft

Metric Sizes

Living Area: 59.1 m2
Deck Area : 4.8 m2
Total Area: 63.9 m2

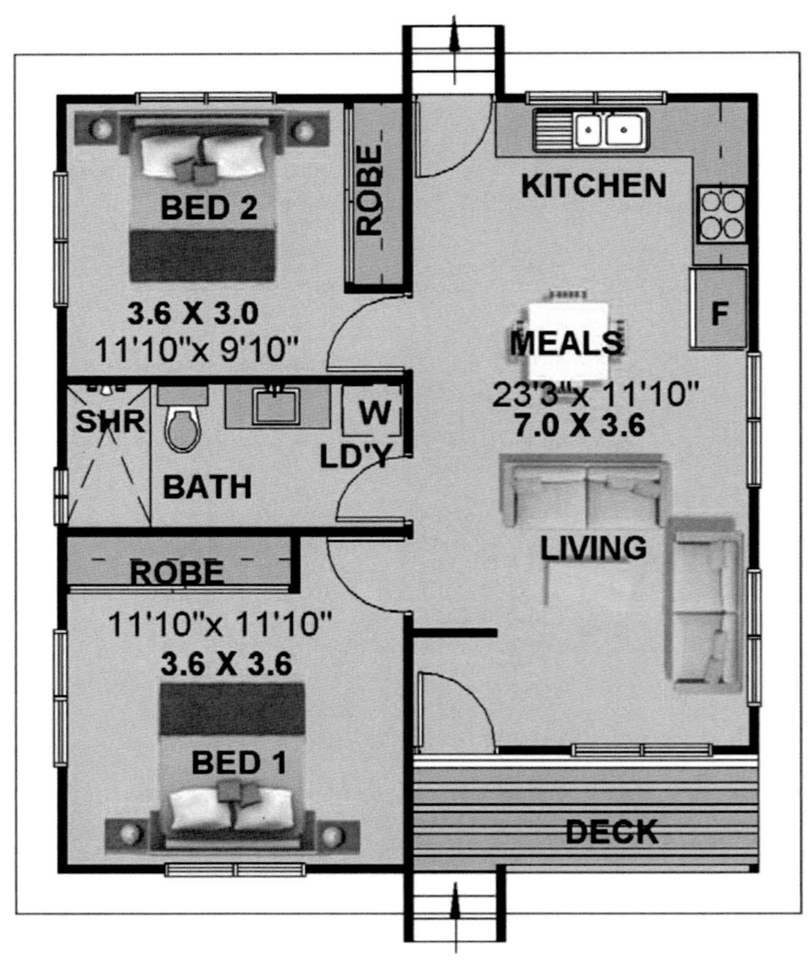

Australian Design Services
A Design World Of Difference

Do you want this plan? See our Website to Upgrade to Our Low Cost Concept Plans

Feet Width 25' x 28 ' **Width 7.4 x 8.5 Meters**

www.australianfloorplans.com.au

Home Design: New Age 63.9 LH   2 Bed + 1 Bath + Large Living

Mirror Plan Left hand Version

FEATURES

- 2 Bedroom
- Large Bathroom
- Kitchen Laundry Combo
- Porch Area

Feet & Inches

Living area : 636 Sq. Ft
Deck Area : 52 Sq. Ft
Total Area: 688 Sq. Ft

Metric Sizes

Living Area: 59.1 m2
Deck Area : 4.8 m2
Total Area: 63.9 m2

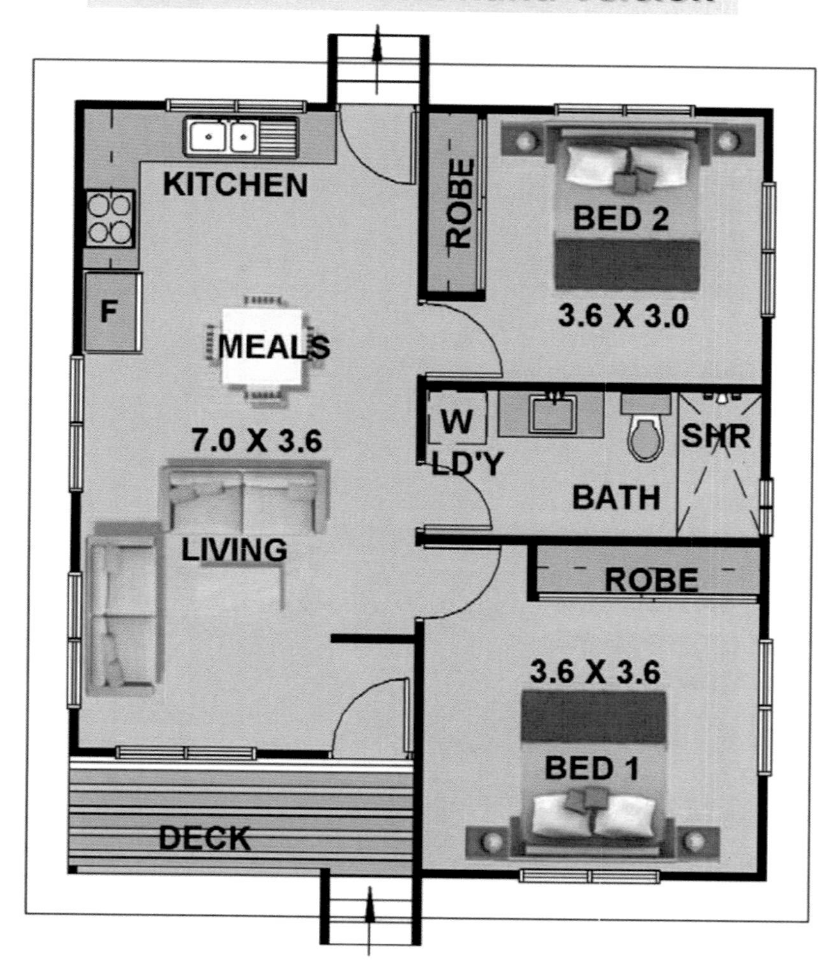

Do you want this plan? See our Website to Upgrade to Our Low Cost Concept Plans

Feet Width 25' x 28 '   **Width 7.4 x 8.5 Meters**

www.australianfloorplans.com.au

Home Design: 63 Wombat

2 Bed + Study + Open Living

FEATURES

- 2 Bedroom
- Study Nook
- Kitchen + Meals
- Open Living Area

Feet & Inches

Living area : 642 Sq. Ft
Porch Area: 42 Sq. Ft
Total Area: 684 Sq. Ft

Metric Sizes

Living Area: 59.7 m2
Porch Area: 3.9 m2
Total Area: 63.6 m2

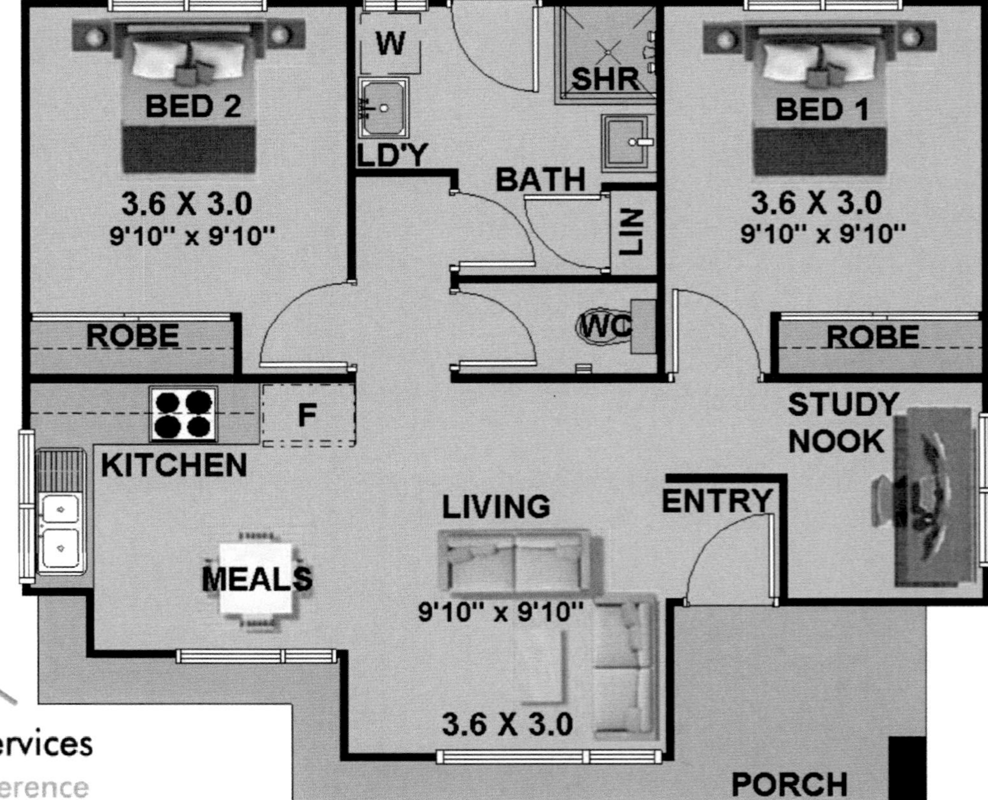

Australian Design Services
A Design World Of Difference

Do you want this plan? See our Website to Upgrade to Our Low Cost Concept Plans

Feet Width 29'11" x 26'7" **Width 9.1 x 8.09 Meters**

www.australianfloorplans.com.au

Home Design: New Age 60 Cottage 2 Bed + 1 Bath + Large Living

FEATURES

- 2 Bedroom
- 1 Bathroom
- Kitchen
- Separate Laundry
- Large Living Area

Feet & Inches
Living Area: 648 Sq Ft
Total Area: 882 Sq Ft

Metric Sizes
Living Area: 59.60 m2
Total Area: 82.65 m2

Australian Design Services
A Design World Of Difference

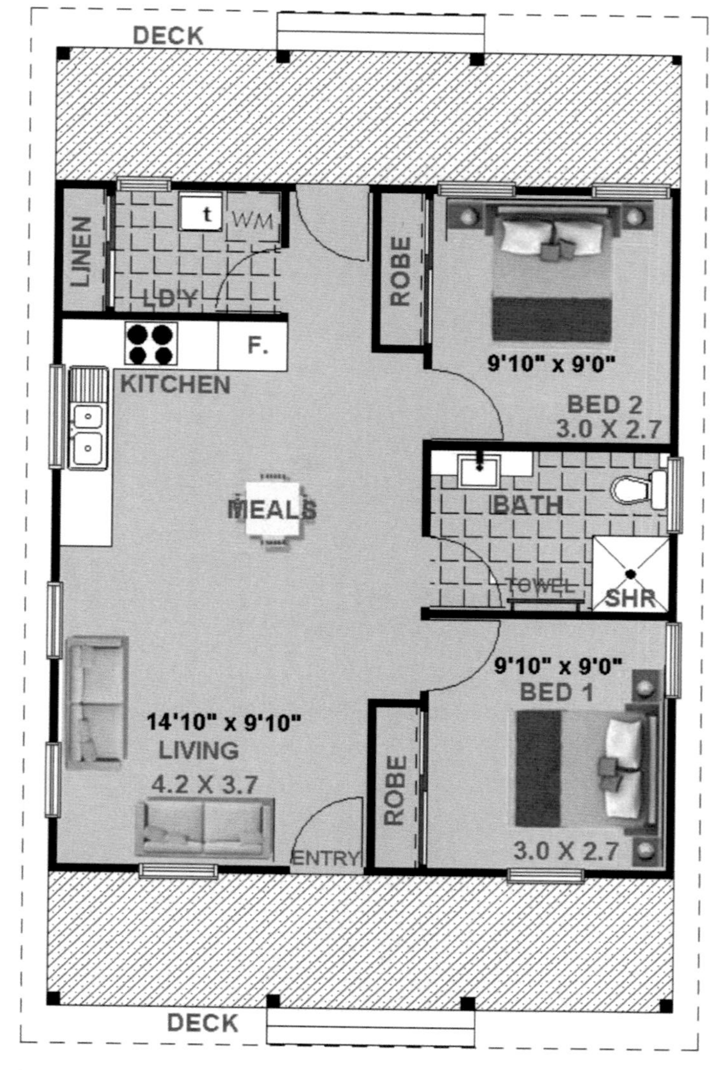

Do you want this plan? See our Website to Upgrade to Our Low Cost Concept Plans

Feet Width 24' x 37 ' **Width 7.25 x 11.40 Meters**

www.australianfloorplans.com.au

Home Design: 73GR-RH

2 Bed + 1 Bath + Alfresco

FEATURES

- 2 Bedroom
- 1 Bathroom
- Kitchen
- Large Living Area
- Alfresco

Feet & Inches

Living area : 810 Sq. Ft
Alfresco : 226 Sq. Ft
Total Area: 1040 Sq. Ft

Metric Sizes

Living Area: 75.28 m2
Alfresco : 21.26 m2
Total Area: 96.55 m2

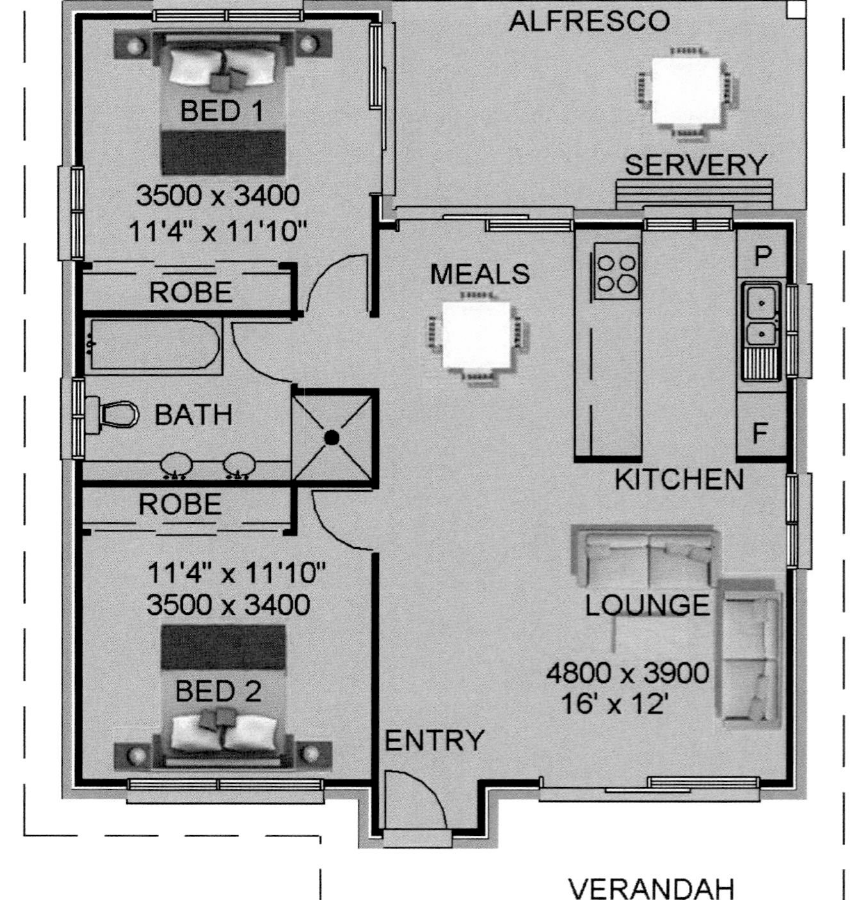

Australian Design Services
A Design World Of Difference

Do you want this plan? See our Website to Upgrade to Our Low Cost Concept Plans

Feet Width 29' x 39'

Width 8.9 x 11.9 Meters

www.australianfloorplans.com.au

Home Design: 73GR - LH **2 Bed + 1 Bath + Alfresco**

Mirror Plan Left hand Version

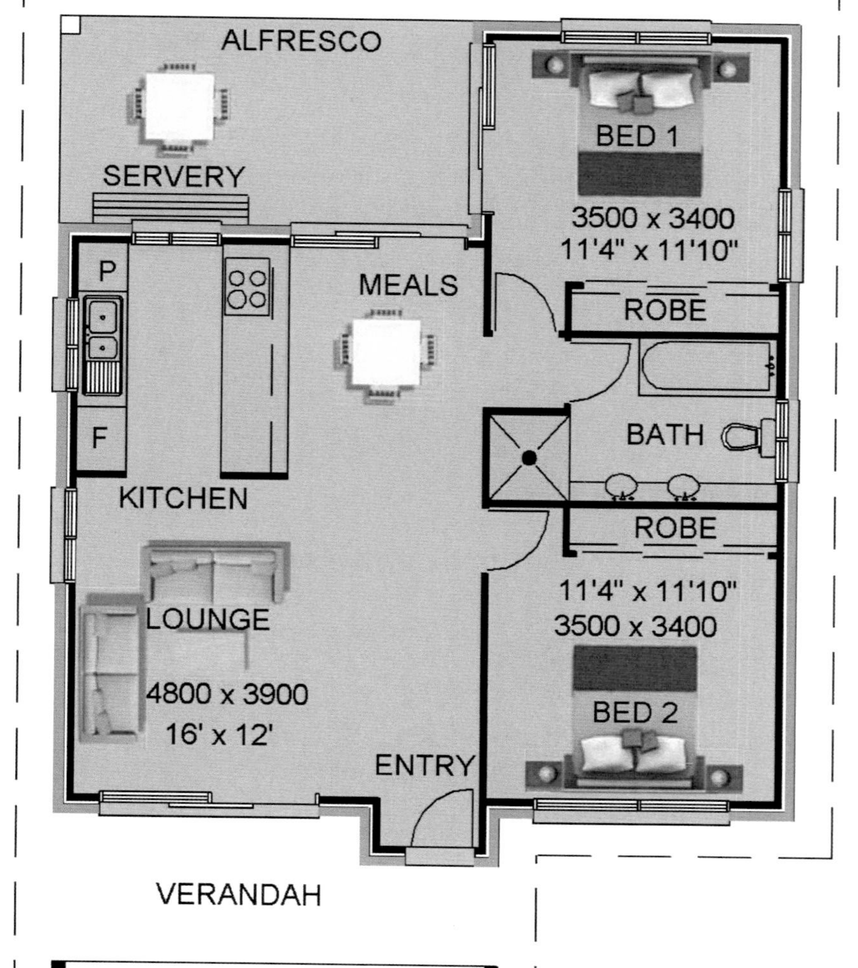

FEATURES

- 2 Bedroom
- 1 Bathroom
- Kitchen
- Large Living Area
- Alfresco

Feet & Inches

Living area : 810 Sq. Ft
Alfresco : 226 Sq. Ft
Total Area: 1040 Sq. Ft

Metric Sizes

Living Area: 75.28 m2
Alfresco : 21.26 m2
Total Area: 96.55 m2

Australian Design Services
A Design World Of Difference

Do you want this plan? See our Website to Upgrade to Our Low Cost Concept Plans

Feet Width 29' x 39' **Width 8.9 x 11.9 Meters**

www.australianfloorplans.com.au

Home Design: 74WH   2 Bed + 2-Way Bath + Deck

Australian Design Services
A Design World Of Difference

FEATURES

- 2 Bedroom
- 2 Way Bathroom
- Open Kitchen
- Large Living
- Front Deck

Feet & Inches

Floor Area: 626 Sq Ft
Deck : 165 Sq Ft
Total Area: 775 Sq Ft

Metric Sizes

Floor Area: 58.74 **m2**
Deck : 15.26 m2
Total Area: 74.0 m2

W.I.R
BATH
W.I.R
BED 1
3.2 X 3.0
10'10" x 10'1"
BED 2
3.2 X 3.0
10'10" x 10'1"
F
20'3" x 15'1"
6.0 X 3.6
LOUNGE
KITCHEN
MEALS
DECK
30'7"x 5'2"
8.3 X 1.6

Do you want this plan? See our Website to Upgrade to Our Low Cost Concept Plans

Feet Width 30'7"x 26'2"   Width 9.31 x 7.97 Meters

Granny Flat Plan: 78.8 - 2 Bed + Large Bath + Large Living

Feet & Inches
Bed 1: 15' 3" x 11' 6"
Bed 2: 8' 9" x 8' 7"
Living: 15'3" x 14' 5"
Floor Area: 557 Sq Ft
Deck Area: 297 Sq Ft
Total Area: 854 Sq Ft

FEATURES
- 2 Bedroom
- Bathroom / Laundry
- Large Kitchen
- Large Living
- Front Deck

Metric Sizes
Bed 1: 4.66m x 3.5m
Bed 2: 2.67m x 2.62m
Living: 4.4m x 4.6 m
Floor Area: 51.8 m2
Deck Area: 27.0 m2
Total Area: 78.8 m2

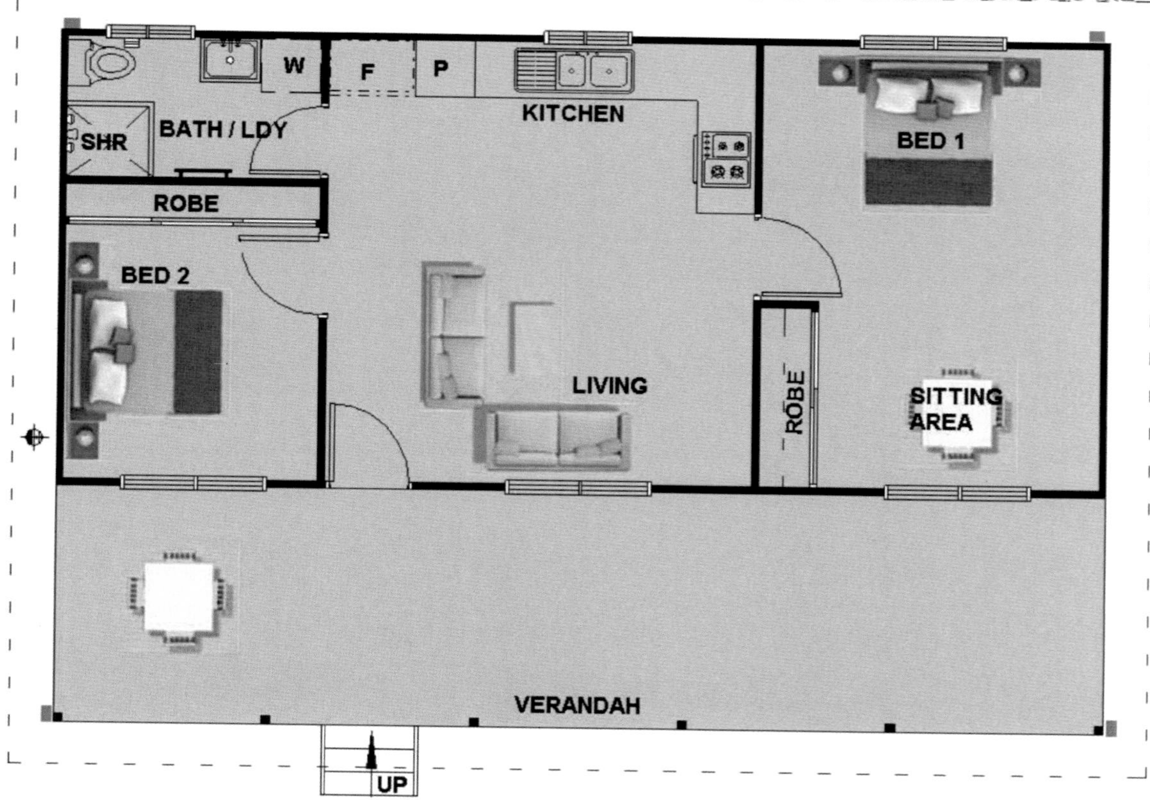

Do you want this plan? See our Website to Upgrade to Our Low Cost Concept Plans

Feet Width 35'5" x 23' 11" **Width 10.8 x 7.3 Meters**

www.australianfloorplans.com.au

Home Design: 80KR 2 Bed + Bath + Separate Laundry

FEATURES

- 2 Bedroom
- Large Bathroom
- Open Kitchen
- Large Living
- Separate Laundry

Feet & Inches

Floor Area: 1023 Sq Ft
Deck Area: 606 Sq Ft
Total Area: 1639 Sq Ft

Metric Sizes

Floor Area: 96.0 m2
Deck Area: 56.33 m2
Total Area: 152.33 m2

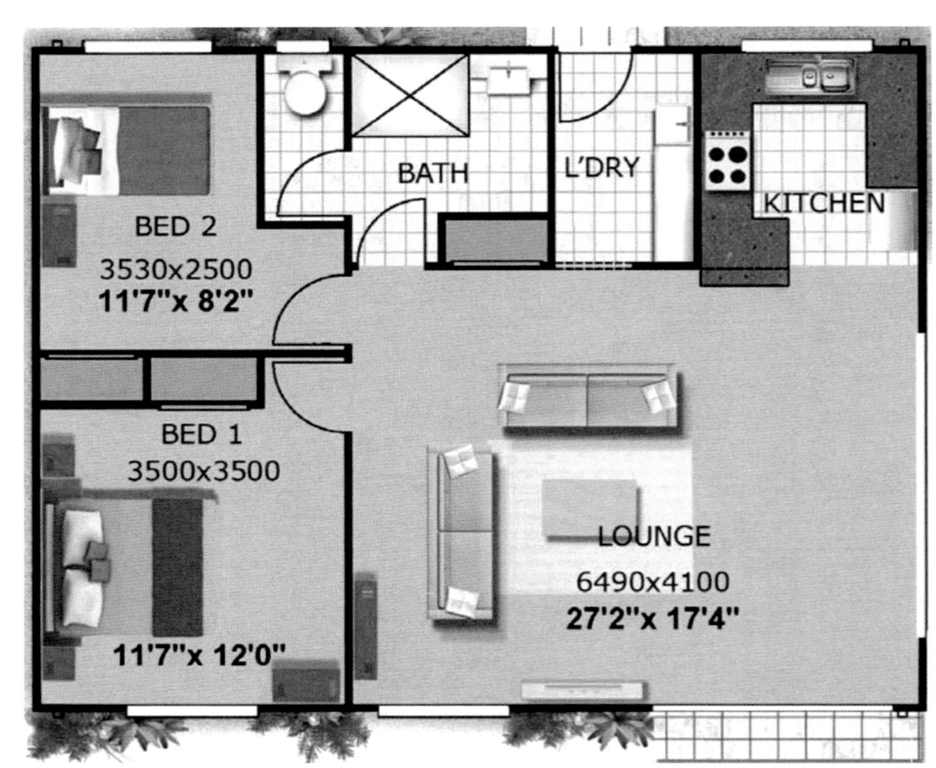

Do you want this plan? See our Website to Upgrade to Our Low Cost Concept Plans

Feet Width 49'3" x 39'4" **Width 12.0 x 8.0 Meters**

www.australianfloorplans.com.au

Home Design: 82.4 RH Skillion **2 Bed + Large Bath + Alfresco**

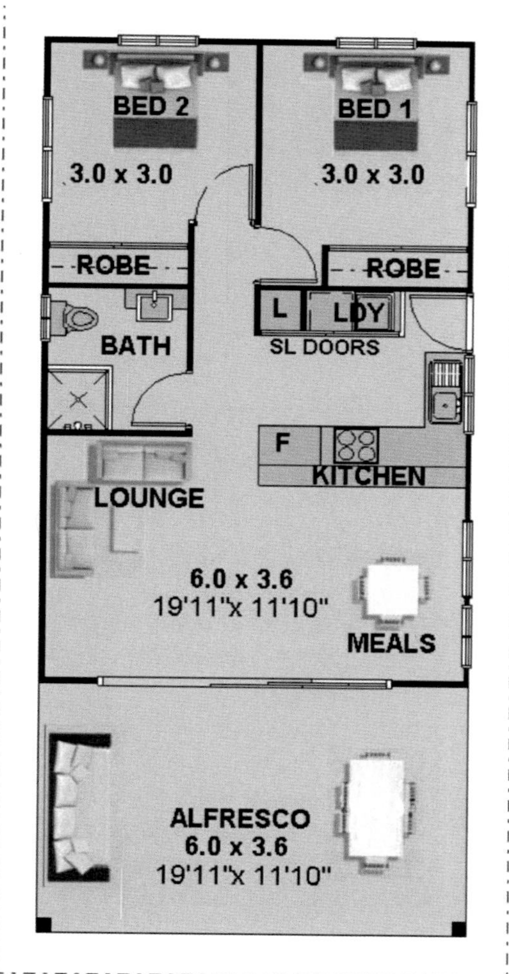

FEATURES

- 2 Bedroom
- Large Bathroom
- Kitchen Laundry Combo
- Alfresco

Feet & Inches

Living area : 639 Sq. Ft
Deck Area : 248 Sq. Ft
Total Area: 887 Sq. Ft

Metric Sizes

Living Area: 59.4 m2
Deck Area: 23.0 m2
Total Area: 82.4 m2

Australian Design Services
A Design World Of Difference

Do you want this plan? See our Website to Upgrade to Our Low Cost Concept Plans

Feet Width 21' x 43' **Width 6.2 x 13.2 Meters**

www.australianfloorplans.com.au

Home Design: 82.4LH Skillion   2 Bed + Large Bath + Alfresco

Mirror Plan Left hand Version

FEATURES

- 2 Bedroom
- Large Bathroom
- Kitchen Laundry Combo
- Alfresco

Feet & Inches

Living area : 639 Sq. Ft
Deck Area : 248 Sq. Ft
Total Area: 887 Sq. Ft

Metric Sizes

Living Area: 59.4 m2
Deck Area: 23.0 m2
Total Area: 82.4 m2

Australian Design Services
A Design World Of Difference

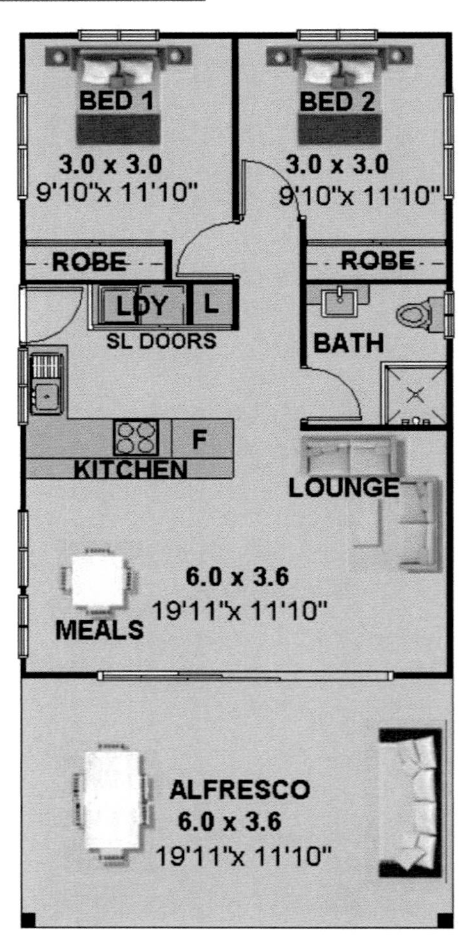

Do you want this plan? See our Website to Upgrade to Our Low Cost Concept Plans

Feet Width 21' x 43'   **Width 6.2 x 13.2 Meters**

www.australianfloorplans.com.au

82.7 RH Hampton's **2 Bed + Study Nook + Deck**

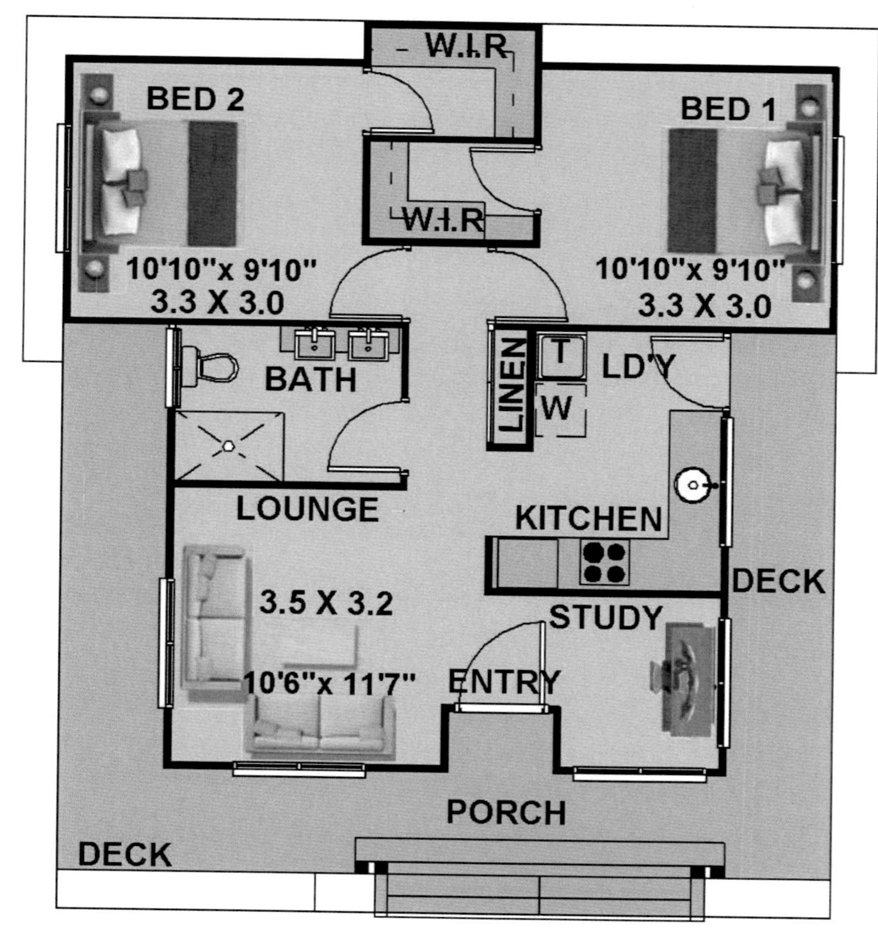

FEATURES

- 2 Bedroom
- Study Nook
- Large Lounge
- Kitchen / Laundry

Feet & Inches

Living area : 644 Sq. Ft
Deck Area: 236 Sq. Ft
Total Area: 890 Sq. Ft

Metric Sizes

Living Area: 59.9 m2
Deck Area: 22.8 m2
Total Area: 82.7 m2

Australian Design Services
A Design World Of Difference

Do you want this plan? See our Website to Upgrade to Our Low Cost Concept Plans

Feet Width 28'8" x 32'7" **Width 8.75 x 9.93 Meters**

www.australianfloorplans.com.au

82.7 LH Hampton's

2 Bed + Study Nook + Deck

Mirror Plan Left hand Version

FEATURES

- 2 Bedroom
- Study Nook
- Large Lounge
- Kitchen / Laundry

Feet & Inches

Living area : 644 Sq. Ft
Deck Area: 236 Sq. Ft
Total Area: 890 Sq. Ft

Metric Sizes

Living Area: 59.9 m2
Deck Area: 22.8 m2
Total Area: 82.7 m2

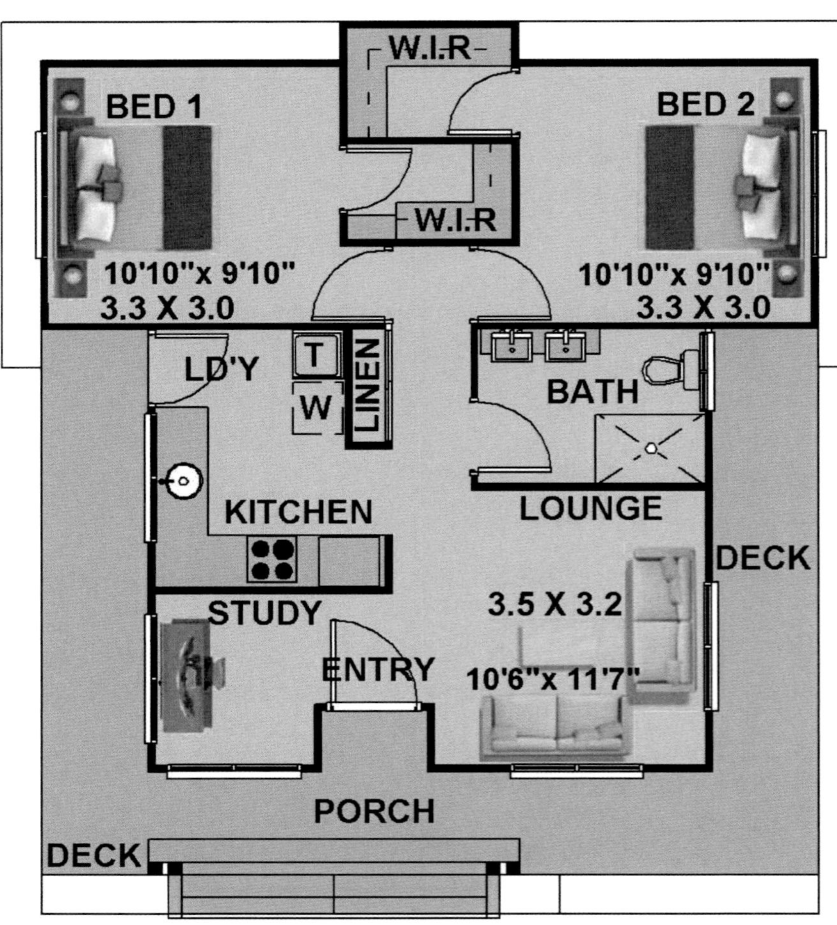

Australian Design Services
A Design World Of Difference

Do you want this plan? See our Website to Upgrade to Our Low Cost Concept Plans

Feet Width 28'8" x 32'7" **Width 8.75 x 9.93 Meters**

www.australianfloorplans.com.au

Home Design: 86.4 RH

2 Bed + Open Living + Large Deck

Australian Design Services

A Design World Of Difference

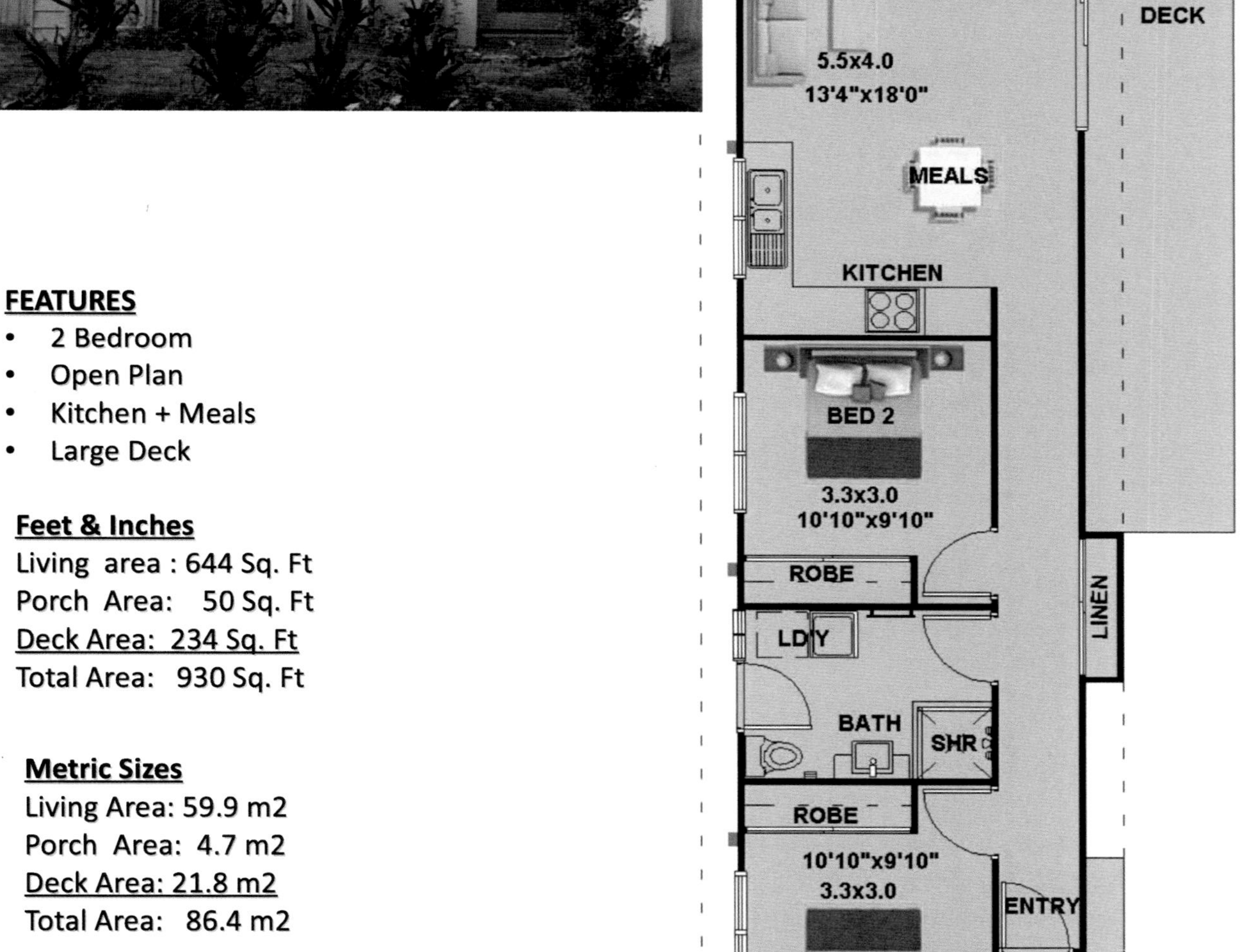

FEATURES

- 2 Bedroom
- Open Plan
- Kitchen + Meals
- Large Deck

Feet & Inches

Living area : 644 Sq. Ft
Porch Area: 50 Sq. Ft
Deck Area: 234 Sq. Ft
Total Area: 930 Sq. Ft

Metric Sizes

Living Area: 59.9 m2
Porch Area: 4.7 m2
Deck Area: 21.8 m2
Total Area: 86.4 m2

Do you want this plan? See our Website to Upgrade to Our Low Cost Concept Plans

Feet Width 19'9" x 53'2" **Width 6.1 x 16.2 Meters**

www.australianfloorplans.com.au

Home Design: 86.4 LH   2 Bed + Open Living + Large Deck

Australian Design Services
A Design World Of Difference

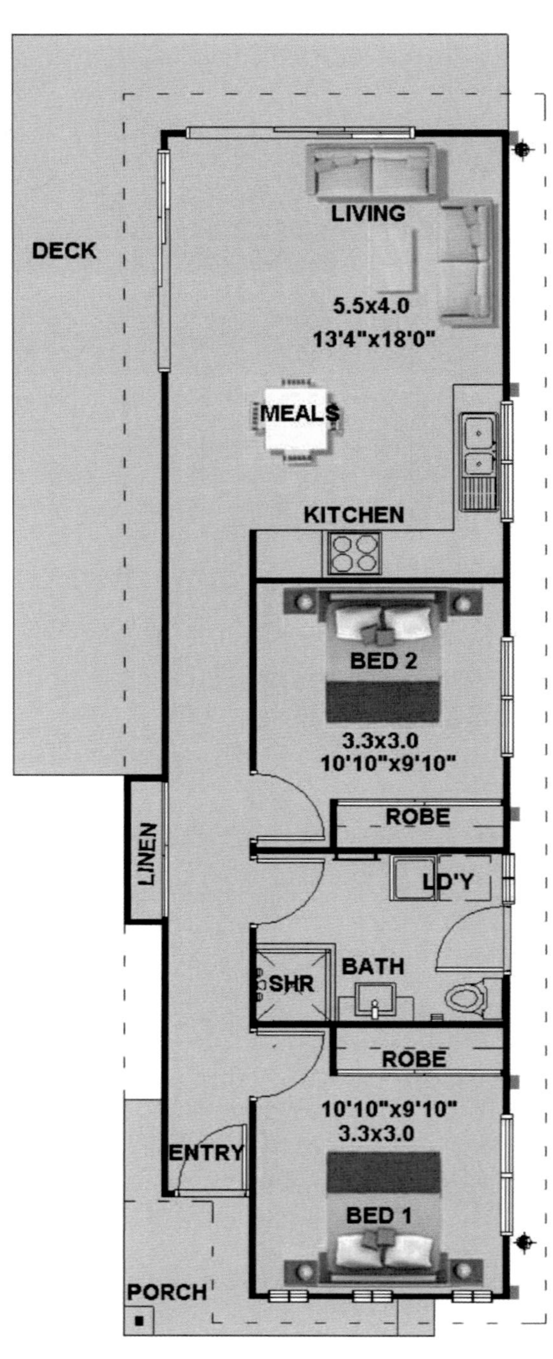

Mirror Plan Left hand Version

FEATURES

- 2 Bedroom
- Open Plan
- Kitchen + Meals
- Large Deck

Feet & Inches

Living area : 644 Sq. Ft
Porch Area: 50 Sq. Ft
Deck Area: 234 Sq. Ft
Total Area: 930 Sq. Ft

Metric Sizes

Living Area: 59.9 m2
Porch Area: 4.7 m2
Deck Area: 21.8 m2
Total Area: 86.4 m2

Do you want this plan? See our Website to Upgrade to Our Low Cost Concept Plans

Feet Width 19'9" x 53'2"   Width 6.1 x 16.2 Meters

www.australianfloorplans.com.au

ROSEMONT COTTAGE DESIGN RH: 88.6 — 2 Bed + 2 Bath

Feet & Inches

Ground Floor: 483.2 Sq Ft
1st Floor : 4470.3 Sq Ft
Total Area: 853.68 Sq Ft

FEATURES

- 2 Bedroom
- 2 Bathrooms
- Kitchen -Meals
- Large Living

Metric Sizes

Ground Floor : 44.9 m2
1st Floor : 43.7 m2
Total Area: 88.6 m2

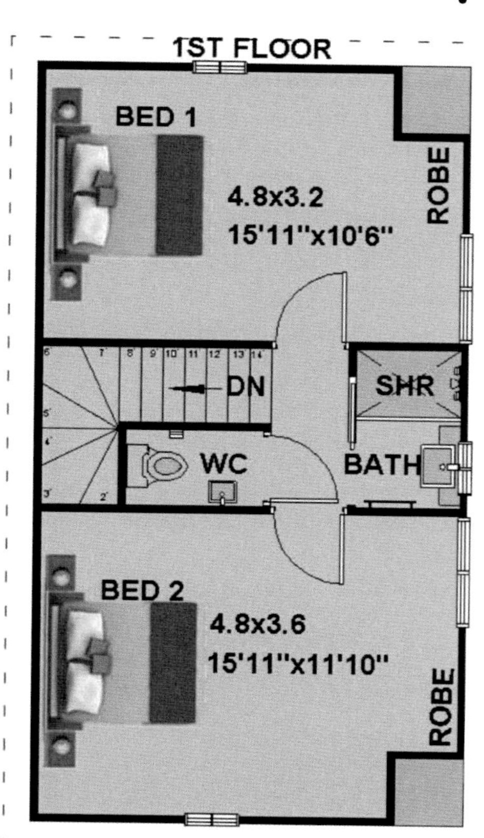

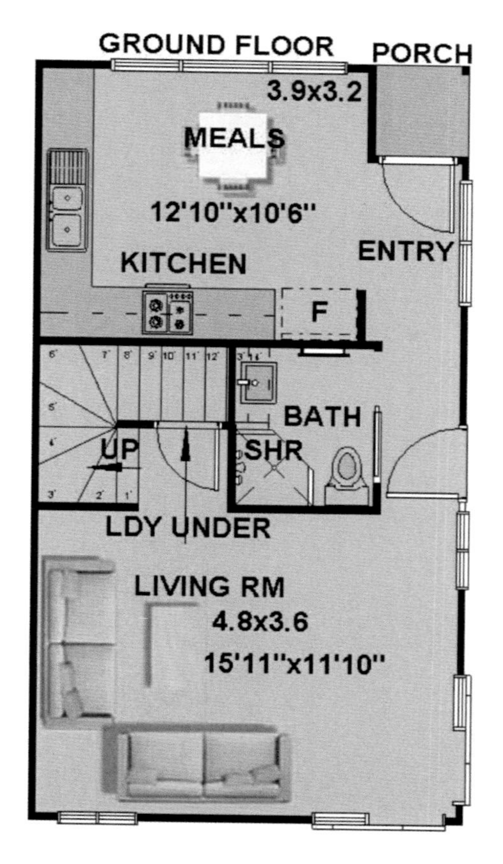

Do you want this plan? See our Website to Upgrade to Our Low Cost Concept Plans

Feet Width 29'6" x 16"5" — **Width 9.0 x 5.0 Meters**

www.australianfloorplans.com.au

ROSEMONT COTTAGE DESIGN LH: 88.6 — 2 Bed + 2 Bath

Mirror Plan Left hand Version

Feet & Inches
Ground Floor: 483.2 Sq Ft
1st Floor : 4470.3 Sq Ft
Total Area: 853.68 Sq Ft

FEATURES
- 2 Bedroom
- 2 Bathrooms
- Kitchen -Meals
- Large Living

Metric Sizes
Ground Floor : 44.9 m2
1st Floor : 43.7 m2
Total Area: 88.6 m2

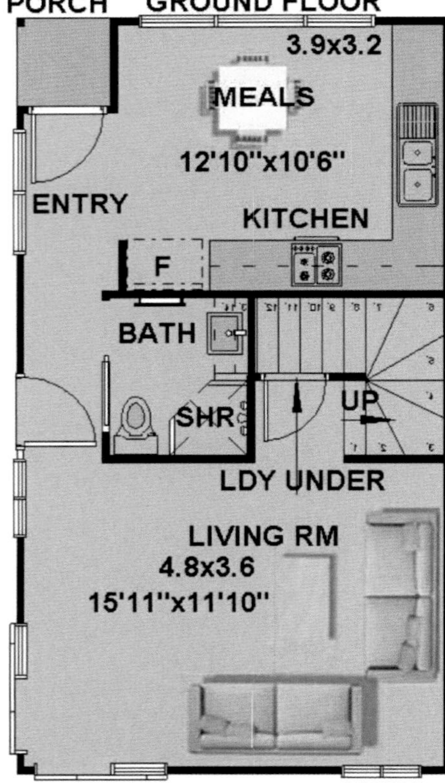

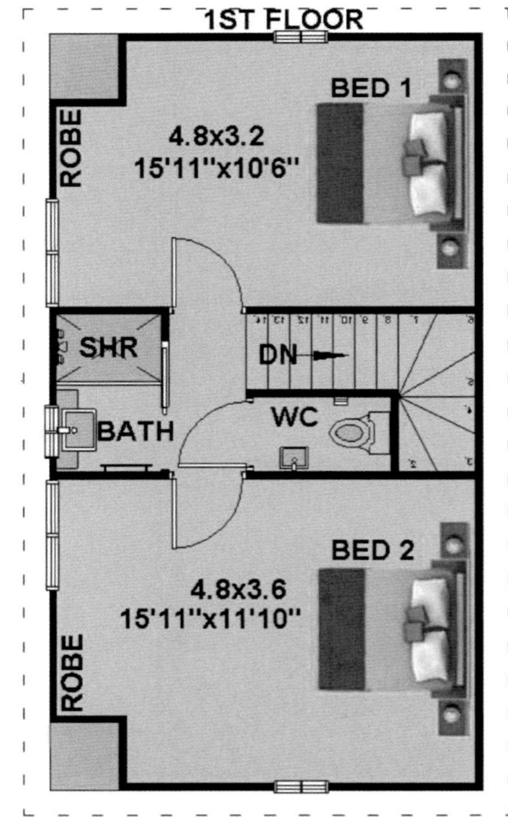

Do you want this plan? See our Website to Upgrade to Our Low Cost Concept Plans

Feet Width 29'6" x 16''5" — **Width 9.0 x 5.0 Meters**

www.australianfloorplans.com.au

Home Design: 89.8 RH

2 Bed + Study + 2 Bath + Deck

FEATURES

- 2 Bedroom + Study
- 2 Bathroom
- Meals Area
- Galley Kitchen
- Large Living
- Separate Laundry

Feet & Inches
Width : 28 '0 "
Length : 34' 4 "
Living area : 644.7 Sq Foot
Total Area : 966.9 Sq Foot

Metric
Living Area: 59.93 m2
Total Area: 89.83 m2

Australian Design Services
A Design World Of Difference

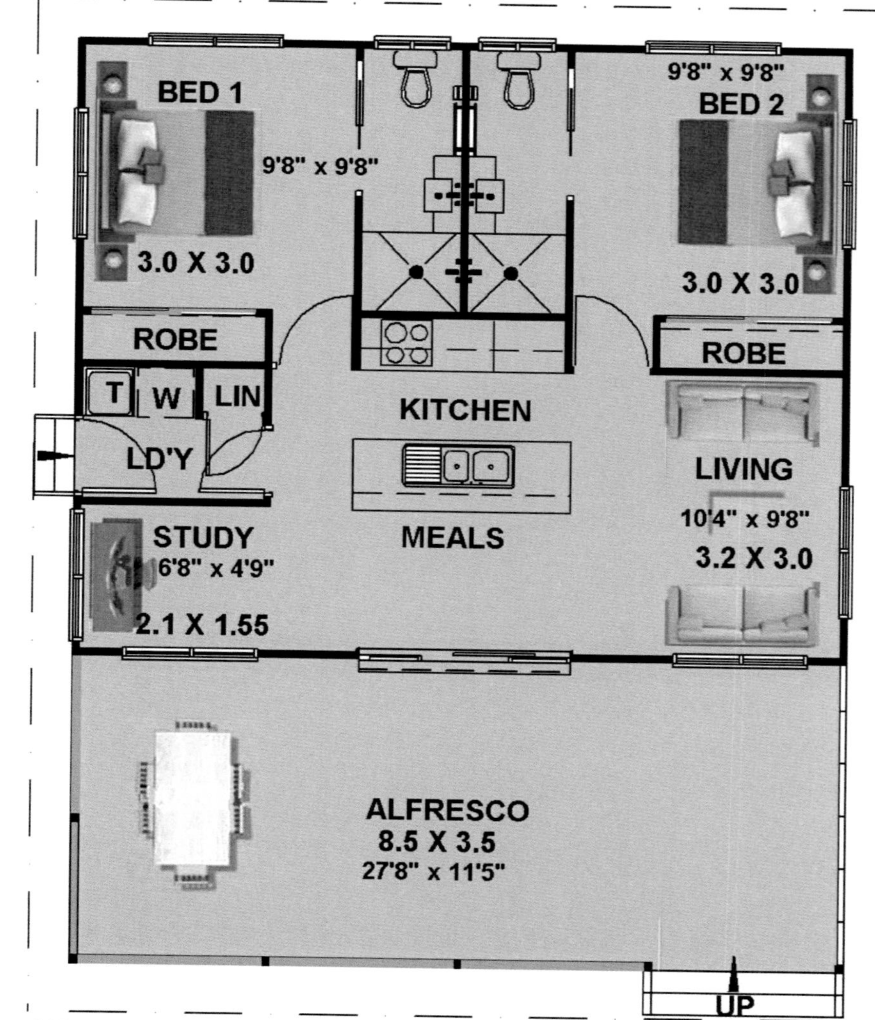

Do you want this plan? See our Website to Upgrade to Our Low Cost Concept Plans

Feet Width 28' x 34'4" **Width 8.55 x 10.51 Meters**

www.australianfloorplans.com.au

Home Design: 89.8 RH

2 Bed + Study + 2 Bath + Deck

Mirror Plan Left hand Version

FEATURES

- 2 Bedroom + Study
- 2 Bathroom
- Meals Area
- Galley Kitchen
- Large Living
- Separate Laundry

Feet & Inches
Width : 28 '0 "
Length : 34' 4 "
Living area : 644.7 Sq Foot
Total Area : 966.9 Sq Foot

Metric
Living Area: 59.93 m2
Total Area: 89.83 m2

Australian Design Services
A Design World Of Difference

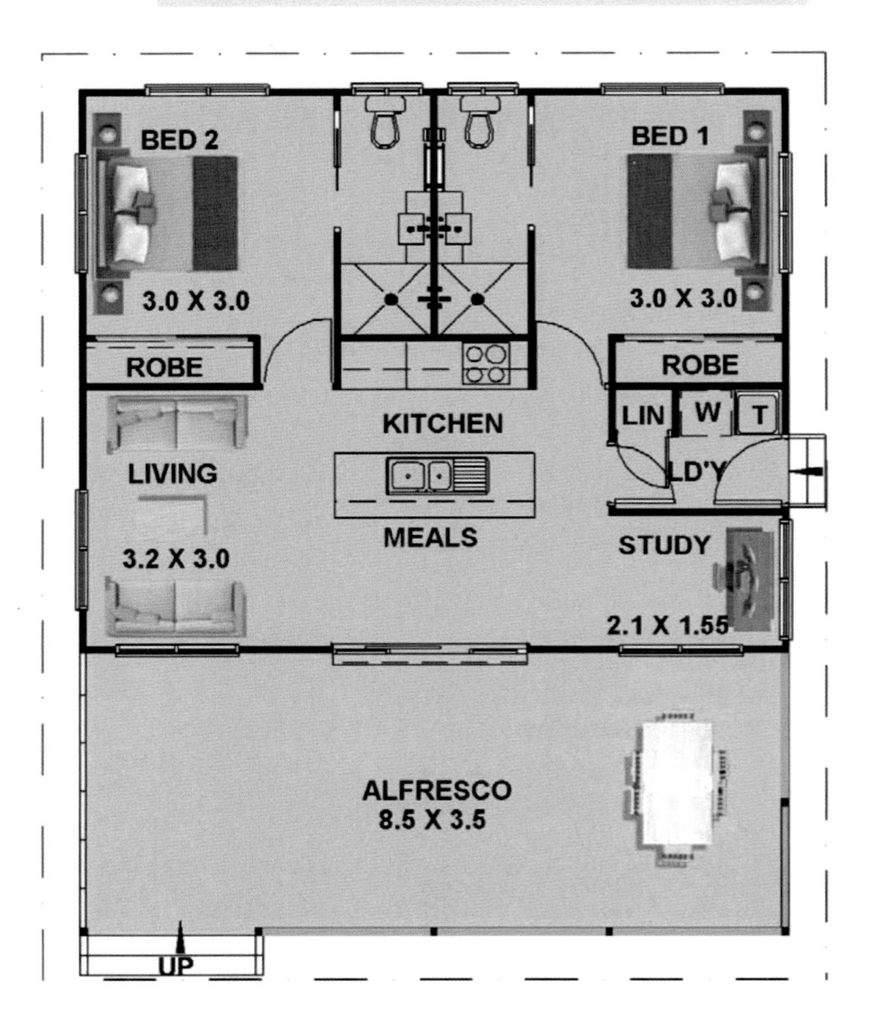

Do you want this plan? See our Website to Upgrade to Our Low Cost Concept Plans

Feet Width 28' x 34'4" **Width 8.55 x 10.51 Meters**

www.australianfloorplans.com.au

Small Home Plan: 90GR - 2 Bed + 2 Bath + Large Living

Australian Design Services
A Design World Of Difference

FEATURES

- 2 Bedroom
- 2 Bathroom
- Separate Laundry
- Large Kitchen
- Large Living

Feet & Inches

Bed 1: 13' 3" x 10' 6"
Bed 2: 11' 6" x 8' 6"
Living: 17'5" x 15' 2"
Floor Area: 961.2 Sq Ft
Verandah : 7.0 Sq Ft
Total Area: 968 Sq Ft

Metric Sizes

Bed 1: 4.04m x 3.2m
Bed 2: 3.5m x 3.0m
Living: 4.6m x 6.1 m
Floor Area: 89.3 m2
Verandah : .70 m2
Total Area: 90.0 m2

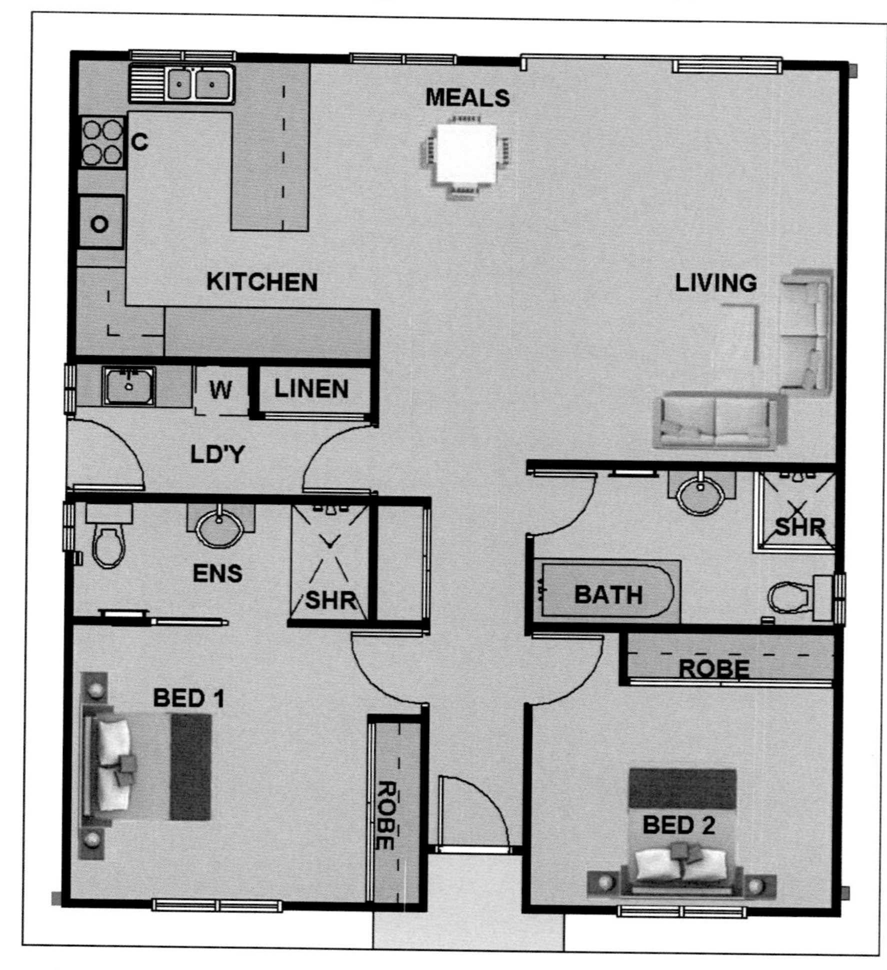

Do you want this plan? See our Website to Upgrade to Our Low Cost Concept Plans

Feet Width 29' 6" x 32' 10" **Width 9.0 x 10.0 Meters**

www.australianfloorplans.com.au

Home Design: 99 Freedom

3 Bed + 2 Bath + Deck

Feet & Inches

Floor Area: 1076 Sq Ft

Deck Area: 200 Sq Ft

Total Area: 1274.0 Sq Ft

FEATURES

- 3 Bedroom
- 2 Bathroom
- Meals Area
- Open Kitchen
- Large Living
- Laundry

Metric Sizes

Floor Area: 99.0 m2

Deck Area: 19.0 m2

Total Area: 118.0 m2

Australian Design Services

A Design World Of Difference

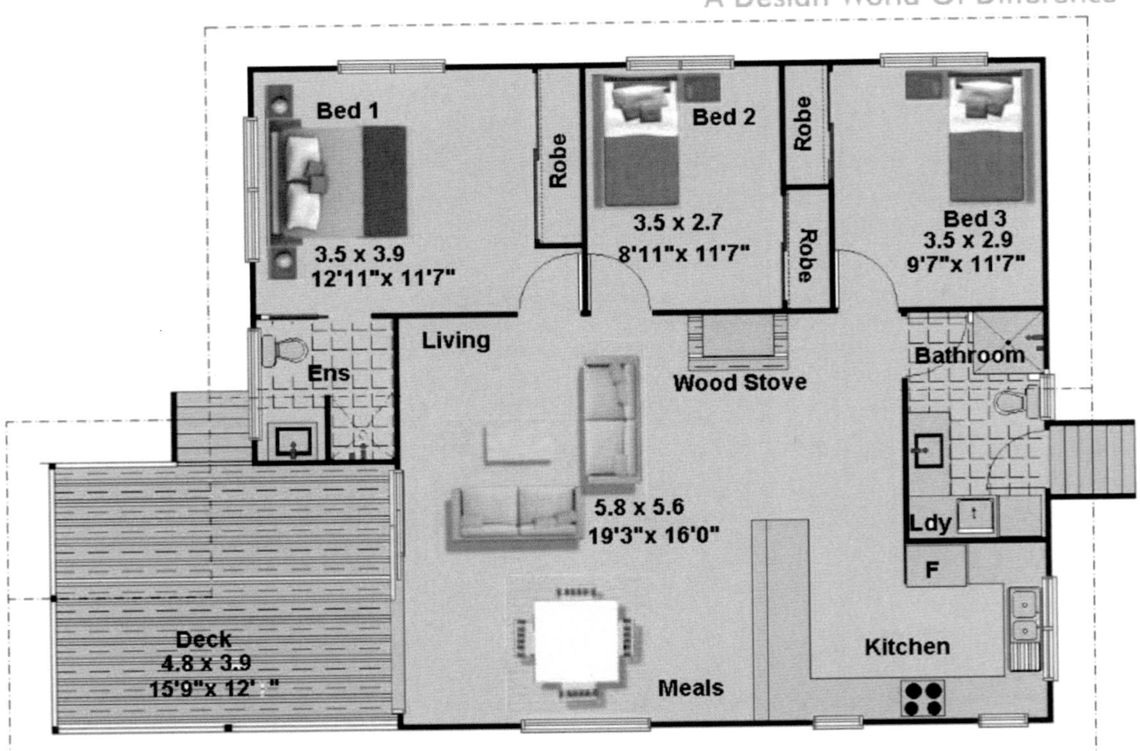

Feet Width 31'6" x 46'2"

Width 9.6 x 14.1 Meters

Small Home Plan: 92.3 - 2 Bed + Large Bath + Large Living

Feet & Inches

Bed 1: 15' 3" x 11' 6"
Bed 2: 8' 9" x 8' 7"
Living: 15'3" x 14' 5"
Floor Area: 894.3 Sq Ft
Verandah : 80.9 Sq Ft
Total Area: 998 Sq Ft

FEATURES

- 2 Bedroom
- Bathroom / Laundry
- Large Kitchen
- Large Living
- Front Verandah

Metric Sizes

Bed 1: 3.75m x 3.3m
Bed 2: 2.6m x 3.3m
Living: 3.7m x 4.9 m
Floor Area: 83.1 m2
Verandah : 7.3 m2
Total Area: 92.8 m2

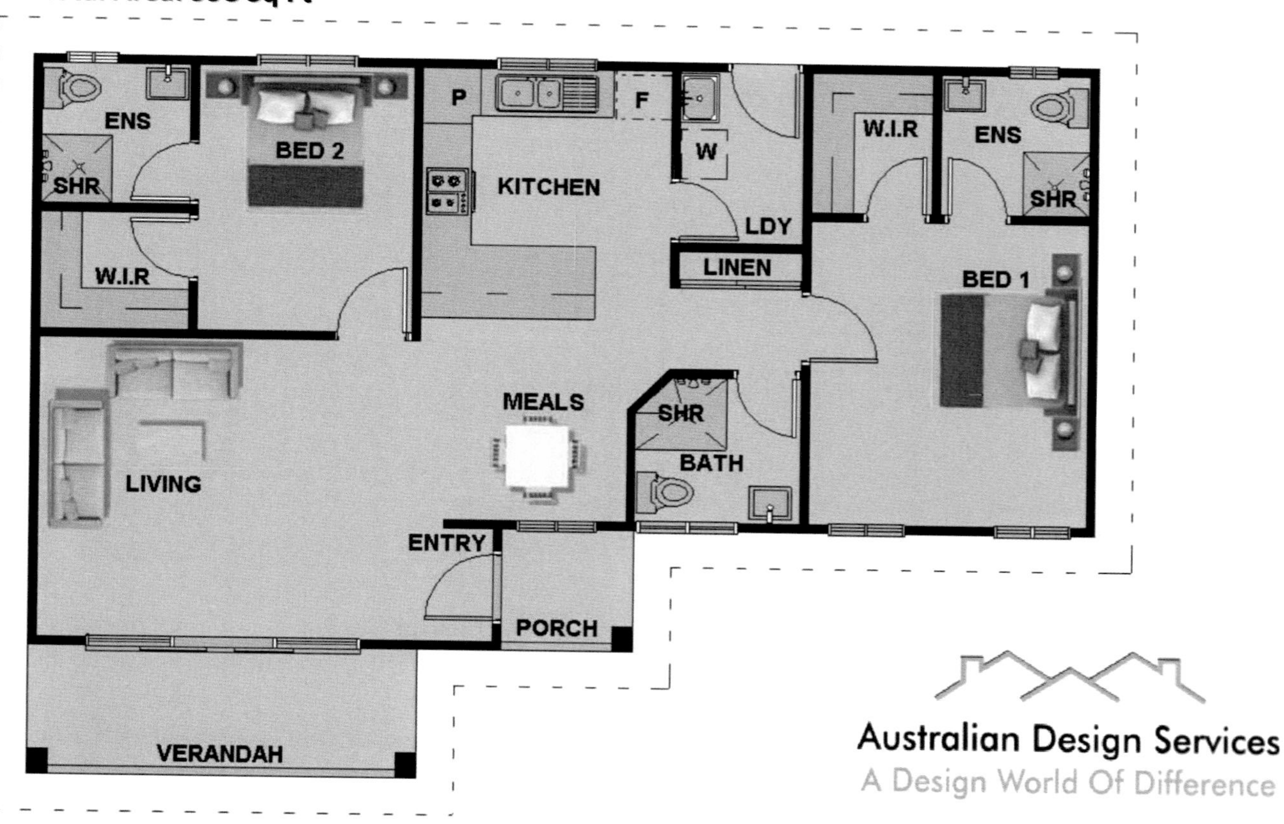

Australian Design Services
A Design World Of Difference

Do you want this plan? See our Website to Upgrade to Our Low Cost Concept Plans

Feet Width 42'2" x 29' 2" **Width 12.85 x 7.3 Meters**

www.australianfloorplans.com.au

Home Design: 93.6 2 Bed + 2 Bath + Large Deck

Feet & Inches
Living Area 827.7 Sq Feet
Total Area 1000.5 Sq Feet

FEATURES

- 2 Bedroom
- 2 Bathrooms
- Open Kitchen
- Large Living
- Large Deck

Metric Sizes
Living Area: 76.9 m2
Total Area: 93.6 m2

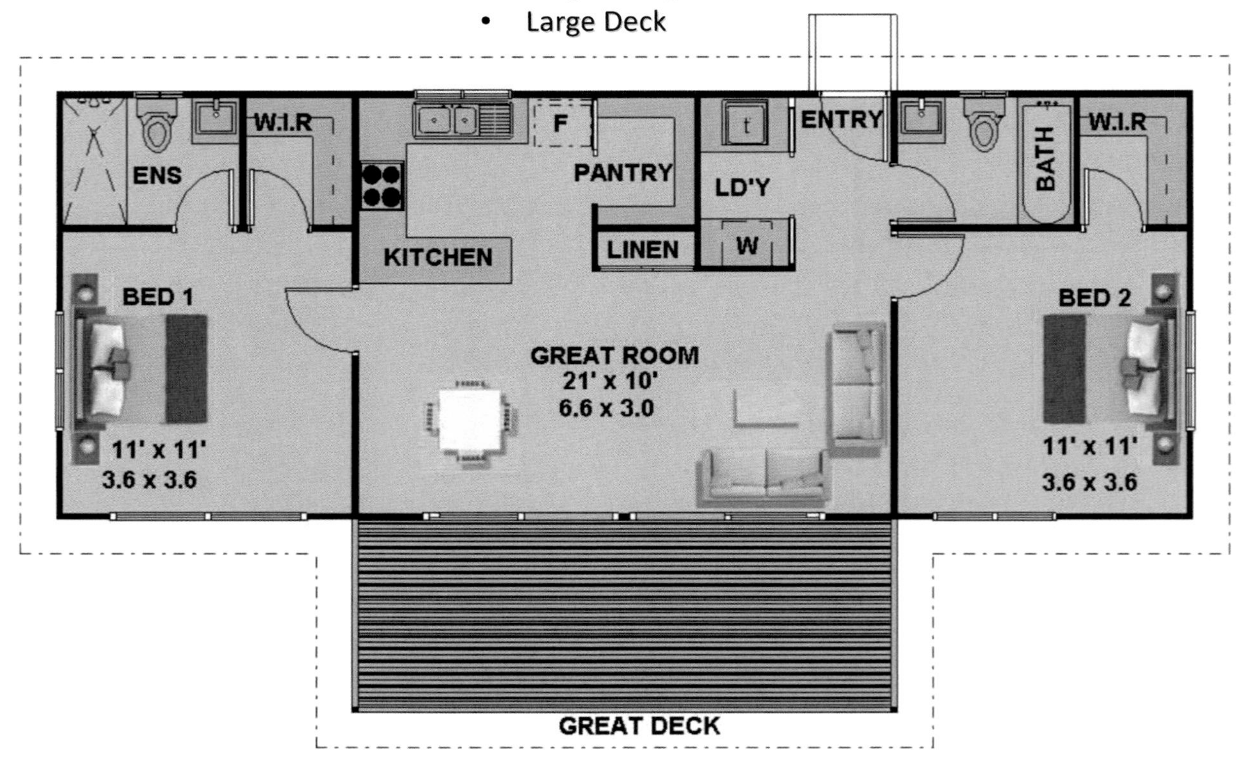

Feet Width 46' 3" x 26' 0" **Width 14.09 x 7.93 Meters**

Home Design: Dragonfly 100 **2 Bed + Study+ Large Deck**

FEATURES

- 2 Bedroom
- Study Nook
- Large Bathroom
- Open Kitchen
- Large Living
- Separate Laundry

Feet & Inches

Living area : 756 Sq. Ft
Deck Area : 320 Sq. Ft
Total Area: 1076 Sq. Ft

Metric Sizes

Living Area: 72.3 m2
Deck Area: 29.7 m2
Total Area: 100.0 m2

Australian Design Services
A Design World Of Difference

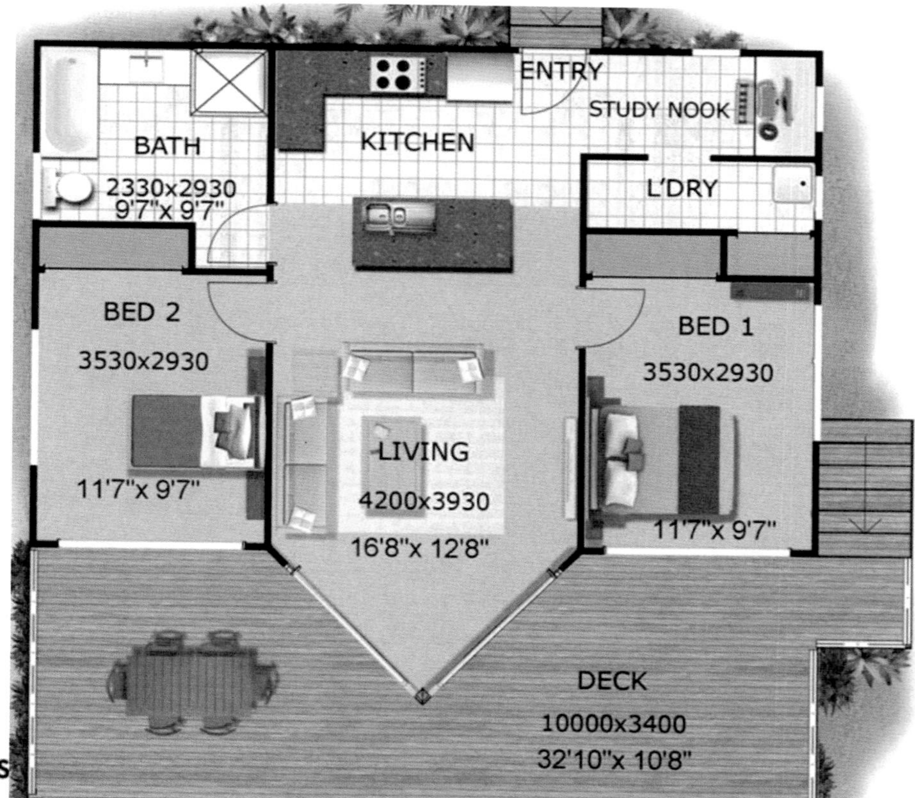

Do you want this plan? See our Website to Upgrade to Our Low Cost Concept Plans

Feet Width 33' Foot x 33' **Width 10.0 x 10.0 Meters**

www.australianfloorplans.com.au

Home Design: 101.2 RH Granny Flat 2 Bed + 2 Bath + Deck

Feet & Inches
Floor Area: 785.7 Sq. Ft
Deck Area: 303.5 Sq. Ft
Total Area: 1089.3 Sq. Ft

FEATURES
- 2 Bedroom
- 2 Bathroom
- Large Living
- Large Deck

Metric Sizes
Floor Area: 73.0 m2
Deck Area:28.2 m2
Total Area: 101.2 m2

Australian Design Services
A Design World Of Difference

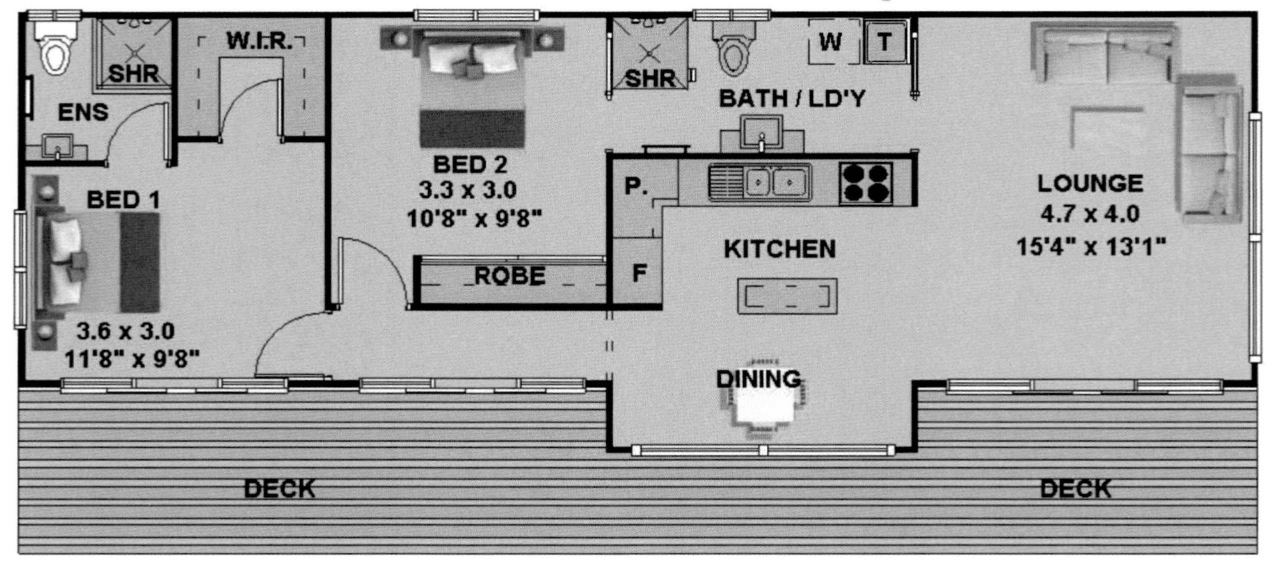

Do you want this plan? See our Website to Upgrade to Our Low Cost Concept Plans

Feet Width 48'7" x 22'3" Width 14.85 x 6.81 Meters

www.australianfloorplans.com.au

Home Design: 101.2 LH Granny Flat 2 Bed + 2 Bath + Deck

Mirror Plan Left hand Version

Feet & Inches
Floor Area: 785.7 Sq. Ft
Deck Area: 303.5 Sq. Ft
Total Area: 1089.3 Sq. Ft

FEATURES
- 2 Bedroom
- 2 Bathroom
- Large Living
- Large Deck

Metric Sizes
Floor Area: 73.0 m2
Deck Area:28.2 m2
Total Area: 101.2 m2

Australian Design Services
A Design World Of Difference

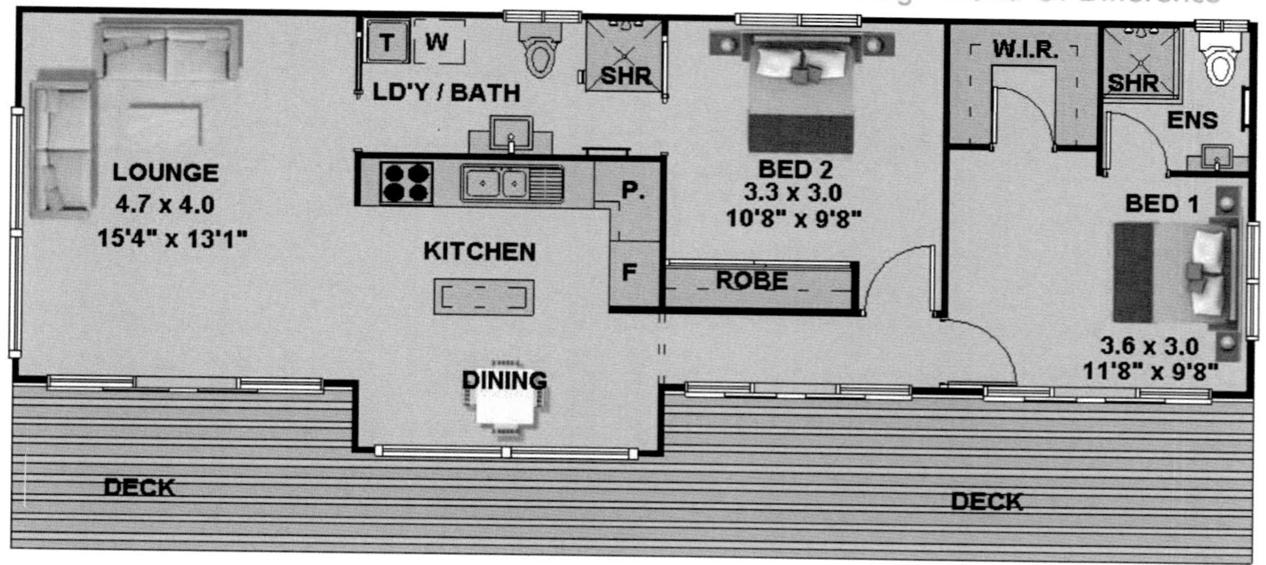

Do you want this plan? See our Website to Upgrade to Our Low Cost Concept Plans

Feet Width 48'7" x 22'3" **Width 14.85 x 6.81 Meters**

www.australianfloorplans.com.au

Home Design: 124.5 Hampton's RH **2 Bed + 2 Bath + 1 Car**

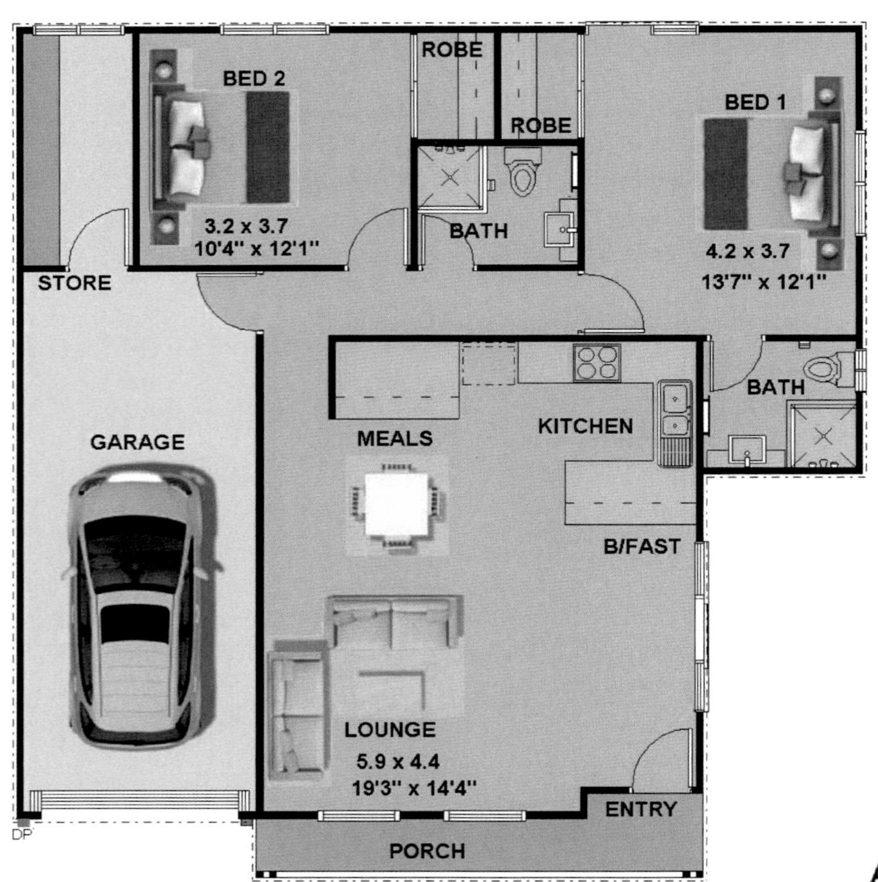

FEATURES

- 2 Bedroom
- 2 Bathroom
- Hampton's Style
- Garage
- Store Rooms

Feet & Inches

Living area : 946 Sq. Ft
Alfresco : 271 Sq. Ft
Total Area: 1340 Sq. Ft

Metric Sizes

Floor area: 87.9 m2
Garage area: 25.2 m2
Total Area: 124.5 m2

Australian Design Services
A Design World Of Difference

Do you want this plan? See our Website to Upgrade to Our Low Cost Concept Plans

Feet Width 38' x 40' **Width 11.6 x 12.0 Meters**

www.australianfloorplans.com.au

Home Design: 124.5 Hampton's LH **2 Bed + 2 Bath + 1 Car**

Mirror Plan Left hand Version

FEATURES

- 2 Bedroom
- 2 Bathroom
- Hampton's Style
- Garage
- Store Rooms

Feet & Inches

Living area : 946 Sq. Ft
Alfresco : 271 Sq. Ft
Total Area: 1340 Sq. Ft

Metric Sizes

Floor area: 87.9 m2
Garage area: 25.2 m2
Total Area: 124.5 m2

Australian Design Services
A Design World Of Difference

ROBE
BED 1
4.2 x 3.7
13'7" x 12'1"
ROBE
BATH
BED 2
3.2 x 3.7
10'4" x 12'1"
STORE
BATH
KITCHEN
MEALS
GARAGE
B/FAST
LOUNGE
5.9 x 4.4
19'3" x 14'4"
ENTRY
PORCH
DP

Do you want this plan? See our Website to Upgrade to Our Low Cost Concept Plans

Feet Width 38' x 40' **Width 11.6 x 12.0 Meters**

www.australianfloorplans.com.au

Home Design:125CLM-RH 2 Bed + 2 Way-Bath + 2 Living Areas

FEATURES

- 2 Bedroom
- Large Kitchen
- 2 Living Rooms
- Double Garage

Feet & Inches

Living area : 971 Sq. Ft
Garage : 350 Sq. Ft
Total Area: 1354 Sq. Ft

Metric Sizes

Floor area: 90.2 m2
Garage : 32.5 m2
Total Area: 125.7 m2

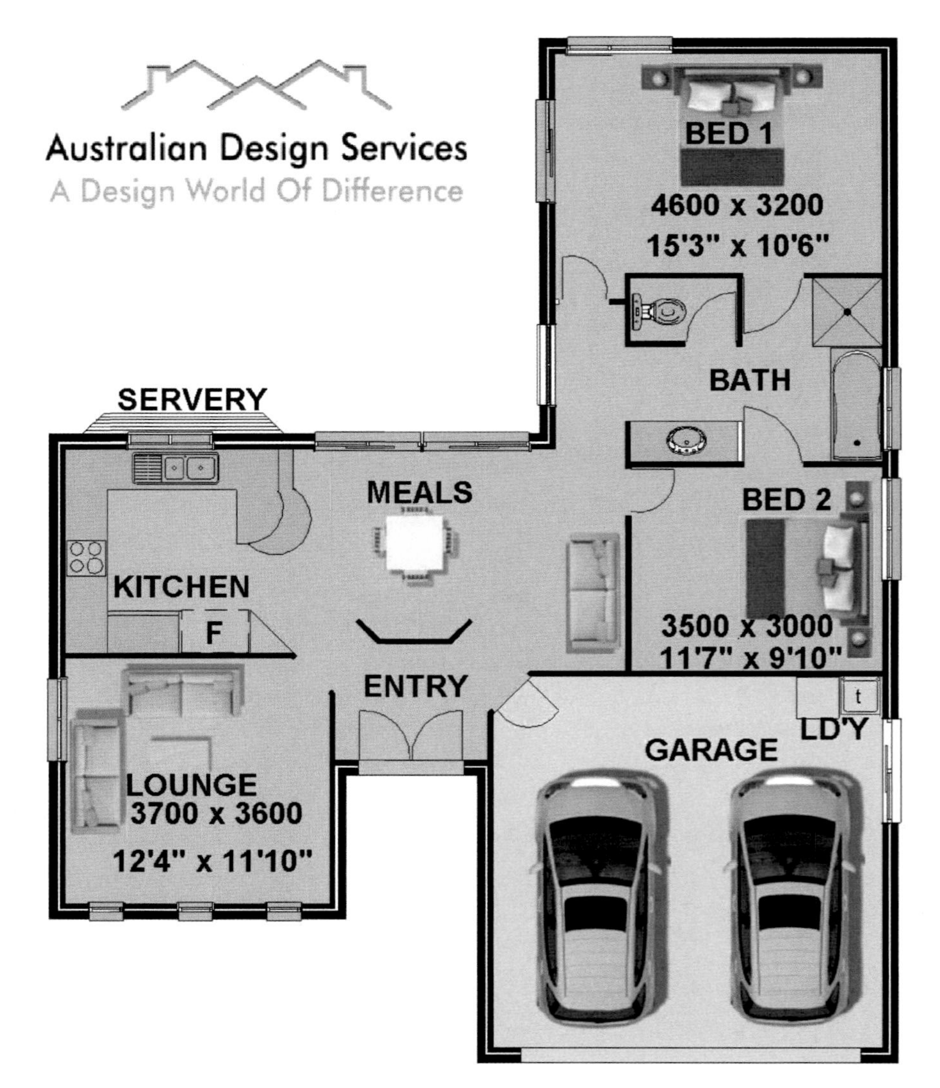

Do you want this plan? See our Website to Upgrade to Our Low Cost Concept Plans

Feet Width 40' x 49' **Width 11.1 x 10.0 Meters**

www.australianfloorplans.com.au

Home Design:125CLM-LH **2 Bed + 2 Way-Bath + 2 Living Areas**

Mirror Plan Left hand Version

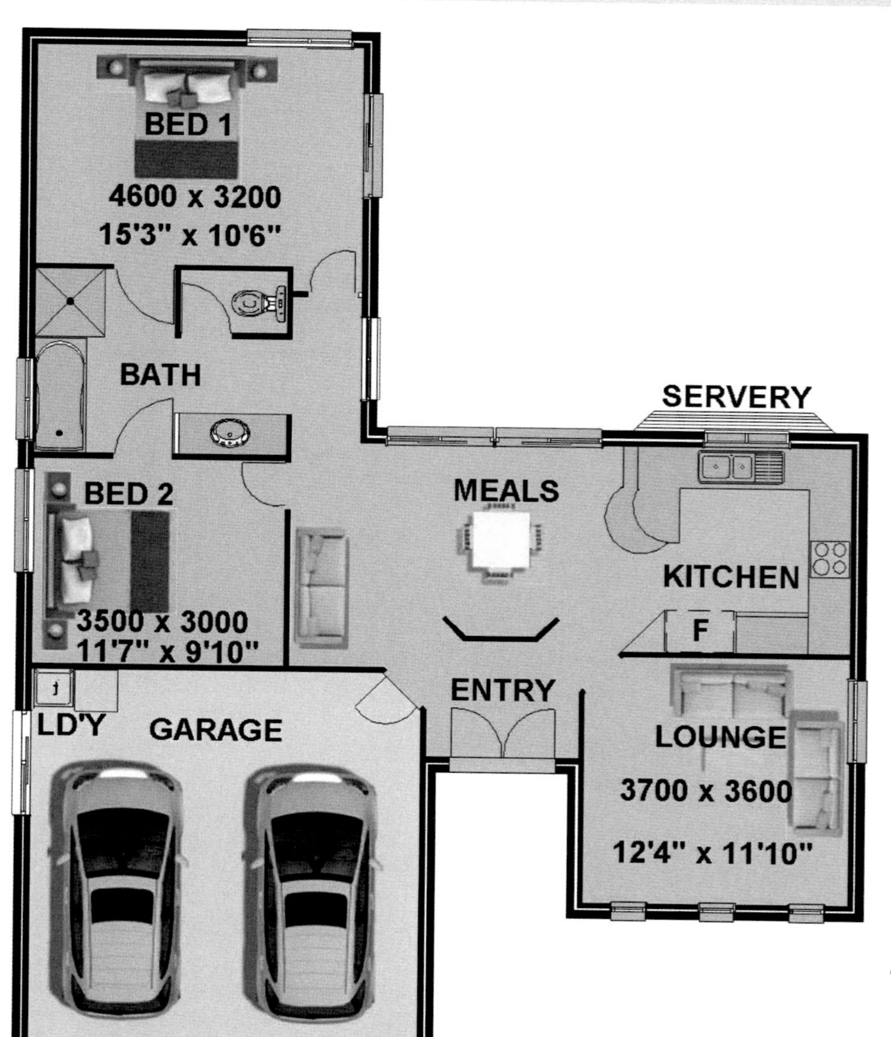

FEATURES

- 2 Bedroom
- Large Kitchen
- 2 Living Rooms
- Double Garage

Feet & Inches

Living area : 971 Sq. Ft
Garage : 350 Sq. Ft
Total Area: 1354 Sq. Ft

Metric Sizes

Floor area: 90.2 m2
Garage : 32.5 m2
Total Area: 125.7 m2

Australian Design Services
A Design World Of Difference

Do you want this plan? See our Website to Upgrade to Our Low Cost Concept Plans

Feet Width 40' x 49' **Width 11.1 x 10.0 Meters**

www.australianfloorplans.com.au

Home Design: 141KR 2 Bed + 2 Bath + Sunken Lounge

FEATURES

- 2 Bedroom
- Kitchen + Dining
- Sunken Lounge
- Large Deck

Metric Sizes

Living Area: 102.6 m2
Total Area: 141.0 m2

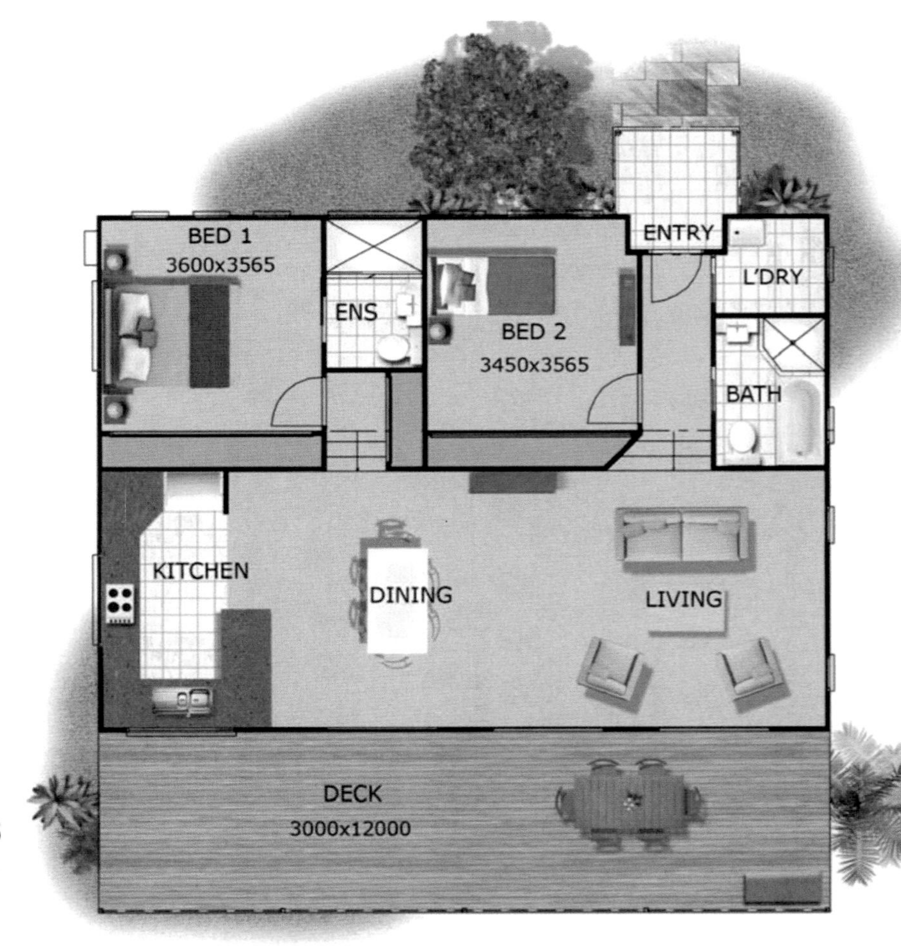

Australian Design Services
A Design World Of Difference

Do you want this plan? See our Website to Upgrade to Our Low Cost Concept Plans

Width 11.1 x 10.0 Meters

www.australianfloorplans.com.au

Home Design: 173KR- Steep Slope Design 2 Bed + Study + 2 Bath

Feet & Inches
Living area : 1432 Sq. Ft
Deck Area : 430 Sq. Ft
Total Area: 1862 Sq. Ft

FEATURES
- 2 Bedroom + Study
- 2 Bathroom
- Suits Sloping land
- Large Deck

Metric Sizes
Living Area: 133.2 m2
Deck Area: 40.0 m2
Total Area: 173.2 m2

Australian Design Services
A Design World Of Difference

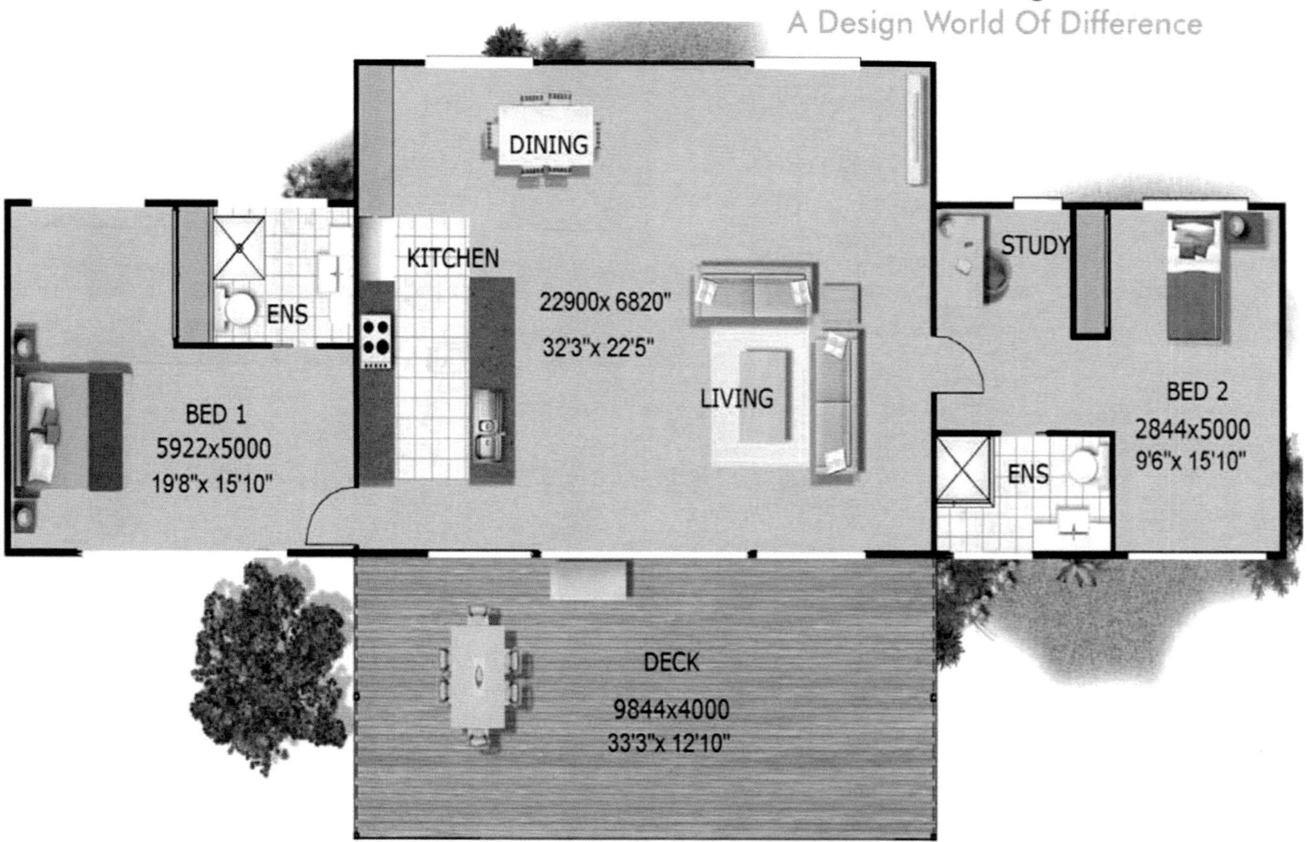

Do you want this plan? See our Website to Upgrade to Our Low Cost Concept Plans

Feet Width 72'2" x 36'1" **Width 11.0 x 22.0 Meters**

www.australianfloorplans.com.au

Home Design: 181.1-RH Country Style Home

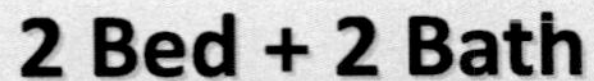

2 Bed + 2 Bath

Australian Design Services

A Design World Of Difference

FEATURES

- 2 Bedroom
- 2 Bathroom
- Large Open Plan
- Large Alfresco

Feet & Inches

Floor Area: 1455 Sq Ft
Porch : 20 Sq Ft
Alfresco : 240 Sq Ft
Deck Area : 212 Sq Ft
Total Area: 1924 Sq Ft

Metric Sizes

Floor Area: 135.4 m2
Porch : 1.9 m2
Alfresco : 23.5 m2
Deck Area: 19.3 m2
Total Area: 180.1 m2

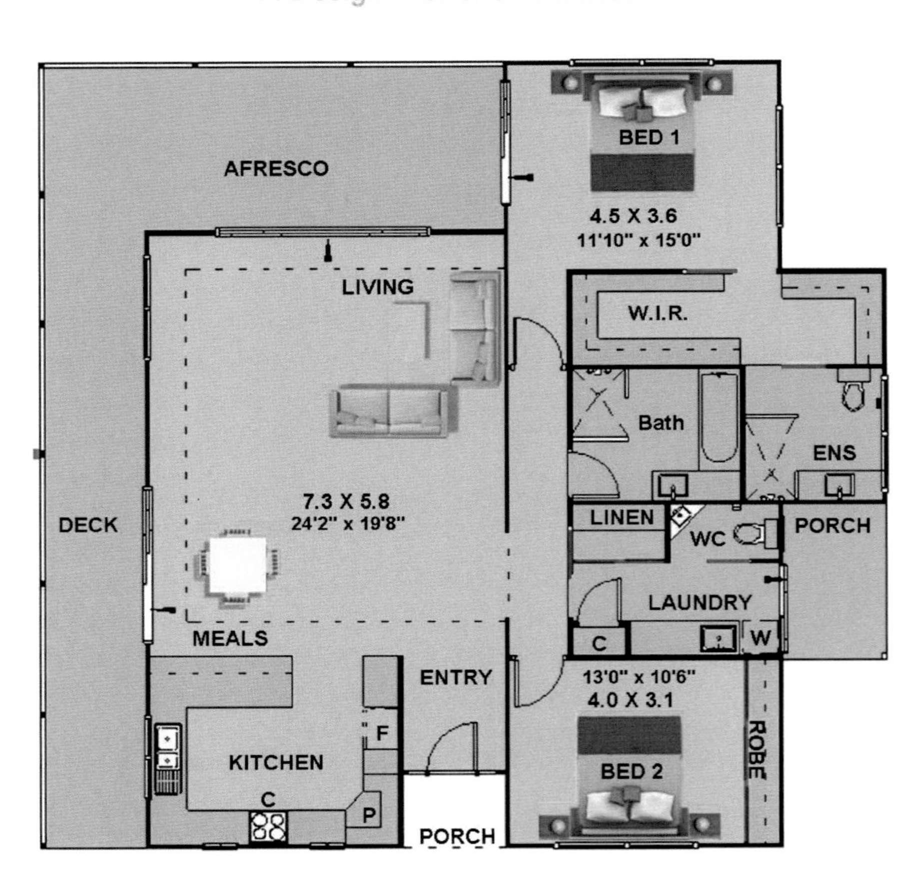

Do you want this plan? See our Website to Upgrade to Our Low Cost Concept Plans

Feet Width 47'1" x 45' 1" **Width 14.34 x 13.74 Meters**

www.australianfloorplans.com.au

Home Design: 181.1-LH Country Style Home 2 Bed + 2 Bath

Mirror Plan Left hand Version

FEATURES

- 2 Bedroom
- 2 Bathroom
- Large Open Plan
- Large Alfresco

Feet & Inches

Floor Area: 1455 Sq Ft
Porch : 20 Sq Ft
Alfresco : 240 Sq Ft
Deck Area : 212 Sq Ft
Total Area: 1924 Sq Ft

Metric Sizes

Floor Area: 135.4 m2
Porch : 1.9 m2
Alfresco : 23.5 m2
Deck Area: 19.3 m2
Total Area: 180.1 m2

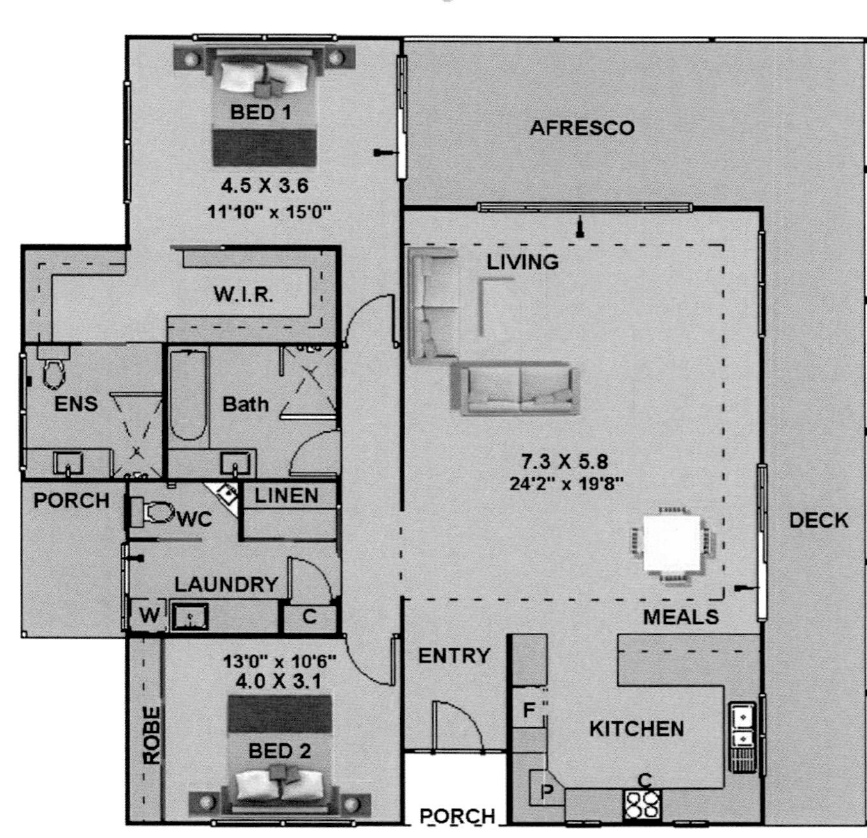

Feet Width 47'1" x 45' 1" **Width 14.34 x 13.74 Meters**

CHECK OUT OUR DESIGN BOOKS

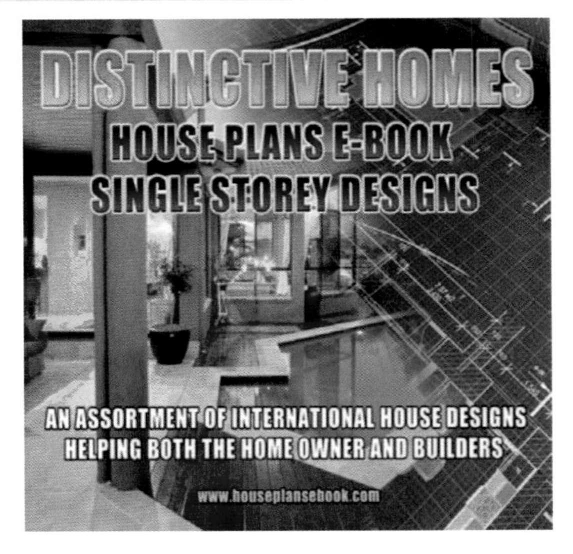

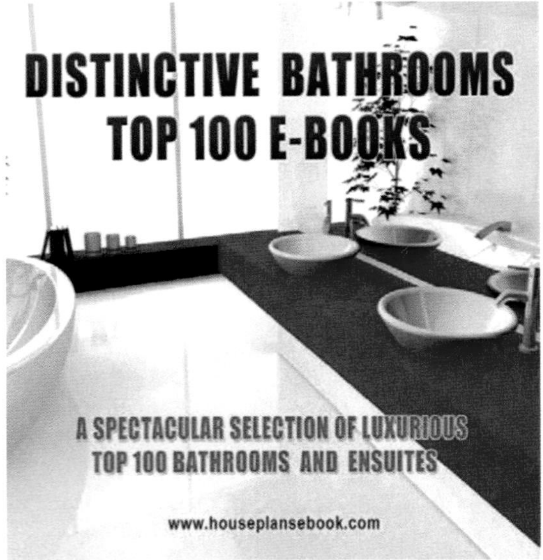

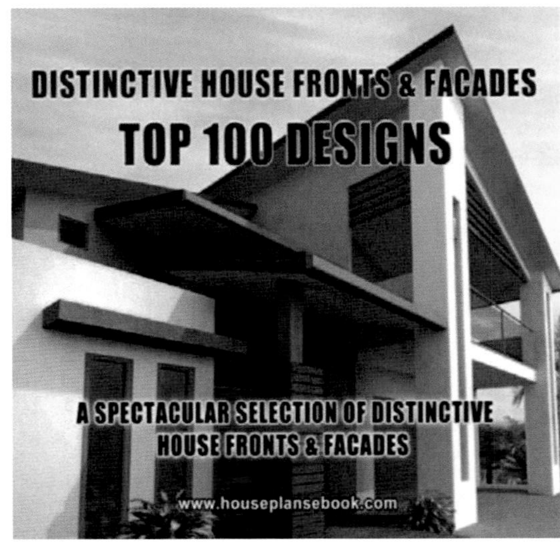

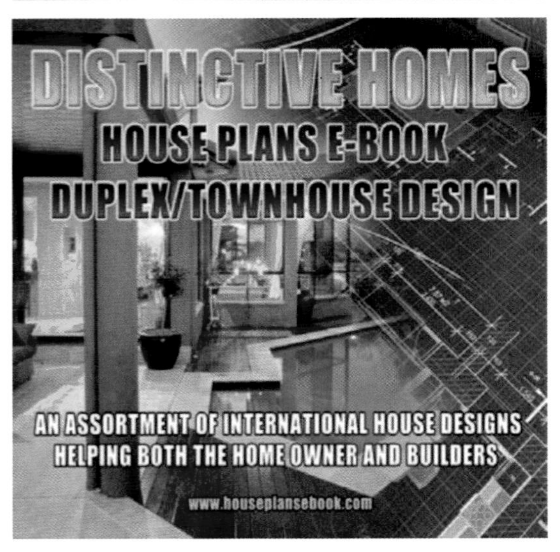

CHECK OUT OUR DESIGN BOOKS

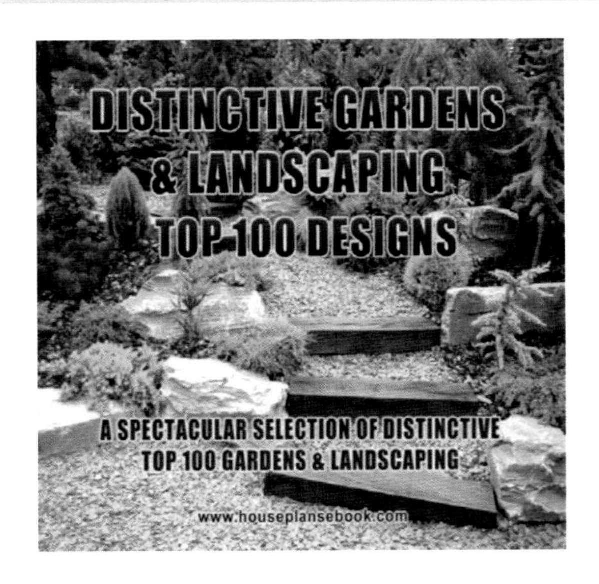

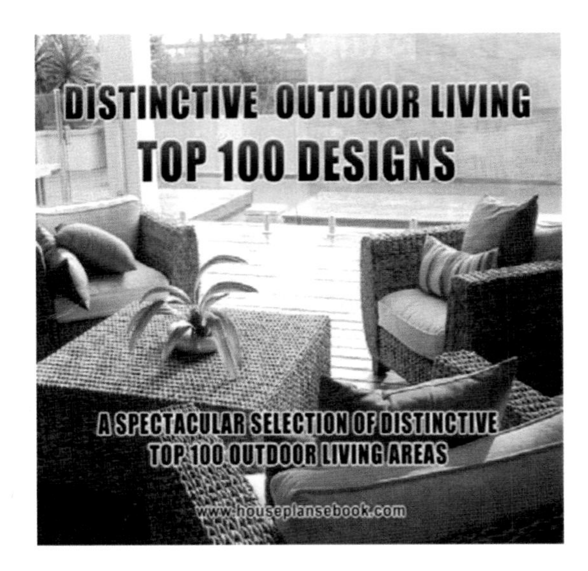

Australian Design Services
A Design World Of Difference

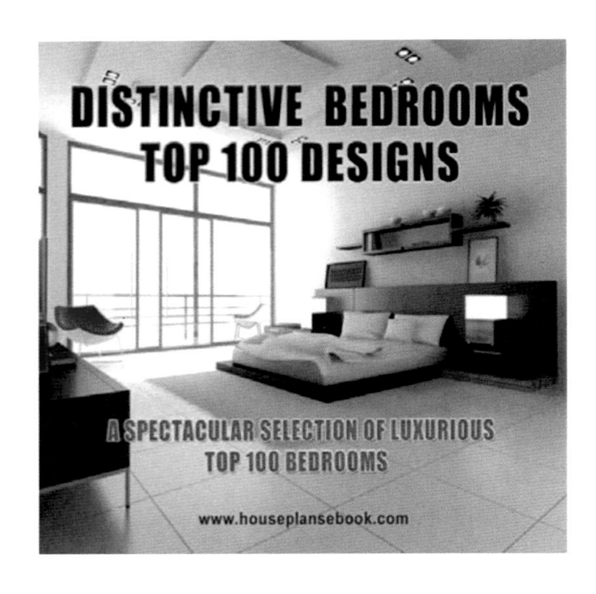

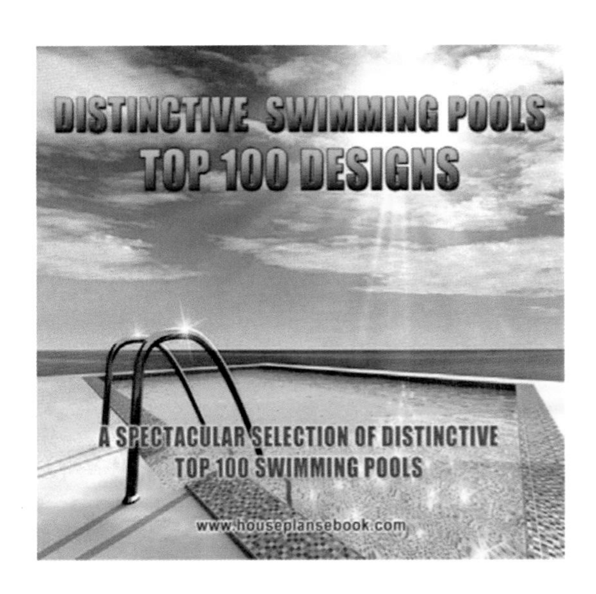

Made in the USA
Las Vegas, NV
25 October 2021